'You're sure he didn't mention that we were once lovers, you and I, Ashley? And that he was contemplating handing you back to me?'

'I knew this would be impossible,' Ashley said in a low, uneven voice, 'So—goodbye, Ross. Any further dealings will have to be through *my* solicitor.'

He caught her at the door. 'Oh, no, you don't. There are some answers I intend getting.'

'Let me go,' she said tightly.

'Do you ever think of those days, Ashley?' he drawled. 'The days when you thought you could outshoot, outride, outdo any man? The days when you were seventeen going on eighteen and you hated yourself, not only because you couldn't outdo me, but also because you found yourself wondering what it would be like to be kissed, held, made love to? Like this . . .'

Books you will enjoy
by LINDSAY ARMSTRONG

HEAT OF THE MOMENT

Serena's first encounter with Sean Wentworth was both misleading and utterly embarrassing. So she was surprised that he offered her the job of governess to his two young nephews, but perhaps he saw it as a chance for her to 'reform'. It didn't matter what he thought, really—as long as she could escape . . .

THE MARRYING GAME

Kirra's encounter with Matt Remington on a deserted beach was an episode she wanted to forget. But her coolness towards him left her when she found out that only he could save her father's failing business . . . and only she could pay the price!

A LOVE AFFAIR

BY

LINDSAY ARMSTRONG

MILLS & BOON LIMITED
ETON HOUSE   18-24 PARADISE ROAD
RICHMOND   SURREY   TW9 1SR

First published in Great Britain 1989
by Mills & Boon Limited

© Lindsay Armstrong 1989

Australian copyright 1989
Philippine copyright 1989
This edition 1989

ISBN 0 263 76379 X

Set in Plantin 12 on 12 pt.
01–8910–47872

Typeset in Great Britain by JCL Graphics, Bristol

Made and Printed in Great Britain

PROLOGUE

SHADOWS ON A SCREEN

THERE were times when she couldn't remember properly, which made her heart beat faster and her throat go dry with fear. Days and nights when he had no substance and she couldn't recall his face to mind, or his hands, and she wondered if they were right about time healing all.

But as the years went by she learnt that she wasn't forgetting, she never would, that he came to mind when she was least expecting it and sometimes so vividly that it took her breath away. She learnt that the smallest thing could trigger her memory: the heady perfume of summer grass, a horse swishing its tail.

What puzzled her, though, was the memory of that night, the last one, the only one. It was more like a dream than a memory, a dream of two people, one of them herself, but she could see herself . . . like a shadow on a screen.

Yet other things she remembered with perfect clarity: the realisation that she was trapped but with one faint, last hope. The decision, the evasions involved, the drive down the star-lit New England highway to town . . . She could remember his surprise, the way his dark eyes had lingered on her with a faint frown in their depths, every plain piece of furniture in the plain flat he rented, the papers spread out on his desk.

She remembered word for word what he'd told her, his hopes and dreams and the fight that lay ahead, and the cup of coffee he'd made her that she'd warmed her hands on because they'd been so cold. She remembered putting the cup down untasted . . . and the silence as they'd stared at each other, what she'd said to break it, the things courage born of despair had allowed her to do.

But that was when the screen always came down and her memories turned to shadows. Shadows of two people kneeling, facing each other, the shadow of a girl with long hair nearly down to her waist and the way her breasts tautened as she raised her arms and lifted her hair off her nape and then let it sink back like a long, dark, billowing curtain, his shadow looming over her, then the two becoming one . . . locked together.

Sometimes she mused that she'd dreamt about it for so long, she couldn't afterwards distinguish the dreams from reality, and it perturbed her that, while there were things her body couldn't unknow, her memories of that part of that night carried no pain . . .

As did other memories of the night, memories of lying in his arms afterwards and putting her hand to his lips when he started to say something, and murmuring, 'Not now, just hold me . . .' Of how she'd known he was staring into space with his chin resting on her head, her body cradled

against him. Memories of stealing away later
while he slept.

CHAPTER ONE

'WELL, well! Fancy that.' Pamela Flint said, as she scanned a column of the newspaper. She was in her mid-forties and, although well-groomed, she had a motherly look about her that was apt to be misleading. For, although she was in fact a mother several times over, she was also a shrewd, practical woman, which she'd demonstrated by bringing up her four offspring single-handedly after losing her husband in a car accident.

'Well what?' her employer enquired from across the room where he was lying back in a chair with his feet up on a desk, nursing a mug of coffee in his hands.

'Ashley Crawford is coming home! It says here—Mrs Ashley Lineham, formerly Ashley Crawford of Crawford Downs, is returning to the district for an indefinite stay. She will be accompanied by her four-year-old daughter Susan, and her fifteen-year-old stepdaughter, Natasha. Both girls are said to closely resemble their father Laurence Lineham, who died earlier in the year. As the only child and heir of Jake Crawford, a prominent and respected member of the community, Mrs Lineham inherited Crawford Downs from her father. The property has lain virtually idle since his death . . . I thought he drank himself to death,' Pamela said stringently, raising her eyes from the paper. 'From what I've heard of him, he was an extremely hard, even unpleasant man.'

Ross Reid put down his coffee-mug and raked a hand through his thick, dark hair. 'He was,' he said musingly, 'a right bastard.'

Pamela raised an eyebrow. 'When you say things like that, with no feeling at all, you generally mean them. So you would disagree that he was prominent and respected?'

'He was certainly physically prominent,' Ross drawled with a wry smile that, together with his dark good looks and tall, beautifully proportioned body, was well-known for its ability to wreak havoc in susceptible female hearts in the small but solid agricultural centre where he practised law. 'You know, commanding of presence and voice, and he was also a shire councillor and president of the turf club, etcetera.'

'Mmm, not necessarily indicative of a pleasant nature, however, I agree. Ashley, on the other hand,' Pamela said slowly, 'from what I remember of her, which is from pony-club days when Janine was horse-mad, had the makings of a great beauty. Even at,' she shrugged, 'fifteen, I suppose, that dark hair and those grey eyes and pale skin was attracting attention. But I also remember that she was rather nice, and certainly not given to throwing her weight around as other members of the landed gentry in these parts can.'

Ross looked amused.

'You know differently?' Pamela enquired a shade tartly. 'You seem to know an awful lot about the Crawfords, if I may say so.'

'It would be a bit odd if I didn't,' Ross commented lazily. 'I jackerooed on Crawford Downs on and off for years in my university vacations.'

'Ah!' Pamela's expression changed. 'You've never told me that. How interesting. So you have something solid to base your aversion to Jake Crawford and his daughter on?'

'You could say so,' Ross agreed gravely.

'Well, why didn't you like *her*?' Pamela gazed at him severely. 'Everybody else did.'

He shrugged and said idly after a time, 'Possibly because she didn't show me the . . . nice side of her nature. In fact, in certain respects, she was a lot like her father.'

Pamela frowned. 'How?'

'She made it quite clear I wasn't good enough for her, dear Pam,' Ross said softly. 'Certainly not wealthy enough, nor did I come from a long line of hell-raisers like Laurie Lineham, or from a long line of anything for that matter.'

Pamela stared at him and said finally, 'You're joking, Ross. But was he . . . such a hell-raiser?'

Ross grimaced. 'He had two failed marriages behind him and he was old enough to be her father, but the Linehams supposedly came over on the First Fleet.'

Pamela smiled faintly. 'A lot of our ancestors did—one way or another.'

'Yes, but the likes of the Crawfords and the Linehams have been tilling the soil in these parts and others, or getting other people to do it for them, for a long time now, which is why they tend to stick together probably, and reject upstarts and strangers—particularly for their daughters. You yourself referred to the "landed gentry" only minutes ago, Pam, so you must know what I'm talking about.'

Pamela chewed her lip. 'All the same, I wouldn't have thought it of Ashley Crawford,' she said stubbornly after a moment. Then, 'It must have been rather a bitter experience for you, Ross. And it could be quite awkward, her coming back.'

He stood up and reached for his jacket. 'On the contrary,' he murmured, 'it was probably the best thing that could have happened to me, and it's all history now, so there's no reason why it should be at all awkward.' He came over and sat on the corner of her desk and grinned crookedly at her. 'And even if I do think she's a prize bitch, that's no reason for you not to like her, Mrs Flint, so you can ungird your loins.'

Pamela pursed her lips then smiled reluctantly. 'Very well,' she said mildly.

Ross narrowed his eyes. 'Now what?' he asked.

Pamela looked at him innocently. 'I don't know what you mean.'

'My dear Pam, since you took over this law practice . . .'

'*I* took it over?'

'In the sense that ever since you became my secretary you have organised, mothered, cajoled and subtly got your way on a whole host of matters, including even what I should wear sometimes, I have learnt . . .'

'Ross . . .' Pamela protested, but she was laughing.

'I have learnt,' he continued inexorably, 'that when you get a certain look in your eye and employ a certain meek tone, that is when I should be particularly on guard against whatever it is you have in mind for me.'

'I would never *dream* of interfering with your love-life, Ross Reid,' Pamela stated. 'Although I've told you often enough it's time you settled down and took a wife, who and how is entirely up to you!'

'Thank you. And you won't try to dream up any little schemes to throw Ashley Crawford-Lineham into my company?'

'Certainly not,' Pamela said primly.

'I have your word on that?'

'Ross,' Pamela said dangerously, 'you're due in court in five minutes. I would advise you to be early in case I'm tempted to box your ears in the meantime.'

'Yes, Mum,' Ross said with a wicked glint in his eye. But he added with a more direct and sober look, 'So long as we understand each other, Pam.'

She returned his look and said soberly herself, 'Yes, Ross. Look, I apologise for any . . .'

He stood up and straightened his tie. 'Don't,' he murmured. 'You're worth your weight in gold to me. How are things on the home front?'

Pamela thought for a moment, then she said with a sigh, 'Do you know anyone who would like a perfectly free, perfectly adorable, not quite pure-bred Border Collie pup?'

He laughed. 'I thought you'd got rid of them all.'

'She had eight pups,' Pamela said darkly of the family pet. 'I've got two to go.'

'Then I shall mention it around. See you at lunchtime, unless anything particularly riveting turns up.'

'Yes,' Pamela said, folding up the newspaper and turning her attention to the mail, but as her employer departed she put down the envelope she'd picked up and watched him cross the road and disappear in the direction of the courthouse, thoughtful and unable to immediately dismiss from her mind what she'd just learnt.

And it was with a rueful little smile that she had to acknowledge to herself that she not only regarded Ross as an employer and a friend, but also took an active interest in his career and admired his achievements considerably. For several reasons. As the widow of a motor mechanic who'd brought her as a bride to this country town, she was not unaware of the invisible line that divided the landed gentry and those who serviced them. But, more than anyone she knew, Ross appeared to have transcended

those barriers, and if anyone did remember that he
came to the district originally as a foster child from
an orphanage they never mentioned it. They
certainly seemed to have abandoned their
reservations about entrusting him with their
daughters, she mused, if the succession of beautiful
girls who passed through these doors was anything
to go by. Many of them were undoubtedly the
daughters of rich farmers and graziers.

Moreover, he would be their Member of
Parliament one day, if she was any judge, Pamela's
reflections continued, and she pondered for a
moment on what had surprised quite a few people:
the fact that, after getting a brilliant law degree,
Ross Reid had turned aside some very lucrative
offers and had instead taken over this small law
practice. But time and a lot of hard work had seen
him build it up into a thriving business and, as
Pamela recognised, it was the perfect background
for someone with political aspirations. Indeed, her
boss was already on the shire council.

'Of course, a marriage to one of those daughters
would really cement things,' she murmured to
herself, 'as he must know. What a pity about
Ashley Crawford, but I still find it hard to believe
she was a snob . . .'

She shrugged after a moment and resolutely
turned her attention back to the mail. But the
second letter she opened, from a firm of Sydney
solicitors, caused her to blink several times and
reread it carefully, then to lay it down with an
unusually serious expression.

*   *   *

At about the same time, Natasha Lineham jumped enthusiastically back into the maroon Jaguar, having just opened and closed a set of gates for it to pass through. 'Isn't it exciting?'

Her stepmother grimaced. 'Opening and closing gates? I must warn you there are another four between here and the house. How's Susie?'

'Still asleep,' Tasha said, peering into the back seat. 'She's amazing—put her into a car for more than half an hour and she falls asleep, whatever time of day it is!'

Ashley Lineham smiled. 'It's probably just as well. She would have been cross and cramped by now, otherwise.'

Tasha smiled back. Then she flicked her red-gold plait off her shoulder and frowned faintly. 'You don't seem to be excited, Ashley. Yet you're coming home for the first time for *ages*, to this marvellous property,' she waved an arm expansively, 'and we're going to live here and ride horses . . . it's like a dream come true for me,' she said with engaging candour.

Ashley changed gear as they breasted a rise. 'It's not looking as marvellous as it should,' she said slowly, her grey eyes scanning a sagging fenceline running parallel to the track. 'But I suppose, since my father died, there have only been a series of managers to look after it . . . I should have taken more interest in it.'

'Well, that's what we're going to do now, isn't it? We're going to live here and run the place and . . .'

'Ride horses,' Ashley finished for her. 'Do you

ever think about anything else?' she asked, wryly
but fondly.

'Not often,' Tasha replied with a cheeky grin.
'Daddy used to say I was a chip off the old block.'
A momentary look of sadness clouded her eyes.
'Do you still miss him, Ash?' she asked with a
tremor in her voice.

Ashley took a hand off the wheel and squeezed
Tasha's. 'Yes,' she said quietly, 'of course I do,
Tasha.'

'Is that why you're . . . different?' Tasha asked.
'You have been for days. And sort of . . . worried.
Is it because doing this—leaving Sydney and
coming here—is like cutting the last tie?'

Ashley was silent for a time, then she said
gently, 'I asked you how you would feel about
that, Tasha. You seemed to think it would be a
good idea. Do you regret it now?'

'No,' Tasha said firmly. 'I think it's a good idea
to be starting a new life, sort of. It makes me feel
brave and adventurous, which Daddy always
recommended but . . . well,' she confessed, 'you
don't seem to be in that frame of mind.'

Ashley hesitated, then she said, 'I am, but I
think I told you that Crawford Downs holds some
sad memories for me. I guess I've been thinking
of them. Sorry! I didn't mean to spoil your spirit
of adventure,' she said ruefully.

'Because your mother and father are both dead?
We're in the same boat, aren't we, Ash? That's
strange, isn't it?'

'Yes—unfortunately, my father and I weren't

on as good terms as you and your father became, though.'

'Because he wanted a son? And because he called you Ashley, even though you were a girl?'

Ashley concentrated on her driving for a minute before replying. 'Because,' she said at last, 'he was . . . impossible. He was hard and arrogant, he . . . made my mother's life a misery, he treated me like a boy all my life, then . . . But to put it in a nutshell,' she deliberately lightened her tone, 'we did not see eye to eye a lot. All the same, now I'm here,' she pulled the big car up and stuck her head out of the window and took a deep breath, then turned to Tasha with a grin, 'now I'm here, I realise we had one thing in common at least. I love this place, too, and if it's the last thing I do, I'll get it back on its feet.'

'*That's* the spirit!' Tasha said approvingly as Ashley started the car again. 'How far?'

'About two miles. Now don't forget what I told you about Maggie. Don't let her intimidate you.'

'I won't. When did you last see her?'

'At my father's funeral. She . . . after I married your father, she stayed on here because she'd been the housekeeper here so long, since my parents were married, in fact. Even after my father died, I couldn't persuade her to leave, although with only itinerant managers here, she must have been lonely, but she said she was too old to change her ways and that someone had to look after the house. She . . . adored my mother.'

*　　　*　　　*

'Oh, oh my,' Margaret Spencer said with tears in her eyes. 'And red hair, too!'

'We get it from our father,' Tasha, who was holding a still sleepy Susan by the hand, confided.

'Well . . .'

'Maggie,' Ashley said, 'it's marvellous to see you, and looking so fit!'

'Of course I'm fit,' Maggie Spencer said vigorously, her tearful moment banished. 'It's the leading of a clean life that does it. Plenty of fresh air, good food, exercise and hard work. Now, young lady——' she said to Tasha.

'Oh, I agree with you,' Tasha said blithely. 'I was brought up on just those same sentiments by a succession of nannies and governesses—until Ashley rescued me; but all the same, to be a champion show-jumper, which is what I will be one day, I couldn't have had a better foundation.'

Maggie blinked.

Tasha continued, 'So I'll be really happy to co-operate with you on all those things,' she assured Maggie. 'In fact, we both will, won't we, Susie? Susie,' she added seriously, picking up the smaller girl and hugging her, 'takes a while to get to know people. Daddy always used to say she's a dead ringer for her Mum like that, aren't you, darling?'

Susie hid her face in Tasha's shoulder, and wound her arms around her neck.

'Well . . .' For a second Maggie was lost for words, then she said gruffly, 'I think it's going

to be a real pleasure to have you both,
Natasha . . .'

That afternoon, Ashley and Maggie sat at the
kitchen table drinking tea. Tasha and Susan were
exploring the garden.

'Glad to be home?' Maggie asked softly.

Ashley glanced around. 'Yes. I missed you,
Maggie, so much. I . . .'

'I know,' Maggie broke in and patted Ashley's
hand. 'I also knew that one day you'd come
back—why do you think I stayed?'

'Oh, Maggie!' Ashley blinked.

'There, there,' Maggie said softly, and they
were silent for a time until Maggie added, 'So he
was . . . good to you, Laurence Lineham?'

'Very good,' Ashley said quietly.

'Funny—after two wives, I didn't somehow
think he would be,' Maggie commented. 'But his
daughter, his . . . other daughter loves you, too.'

Ashley smiled slightly. 'She's a honey, Mag.
And she's been through a lot herself. After their
divorce, her mother was killed.'

'Hmm. The little one has a look of you, you
know, despite the red hair.'

'Does she?'

'Also your mother.'

'Maggie . . .'

'Not many people remember your mother,
Ashley,' Maggie continued musingly, 'which is
why it might not strike most, but I see it. Can't
see any of your father in her at all,' she added,

not without quiet triumph.

Ashley lifted her head and stared into Maggie's faded but steady blue eyes. 'No,' she said at last. 'Did he . . . when he died suddenly like that, although I'd sworn . . .' She stopped and bit her lip.

'He never changed one whit,' Maggie said, 'except that he got to feeling sorry for himself.'

Ashley put a hand to her mouth.

Maggie observed this, then said urgently, 'Don't fret, child. I could see at the funeral how you were feeling, but we didn't have the time to talk properly.'

'I know,' Ashley whispered.

'And he could have come to you—perhaps he would have, who knows? But the best you can do is put it behind you now. You're still young, and you've got your life in front of you. You're only twenty-five! And you've done the right thing, coming back to where you belong. We'll . . .' She stopped as the phone rang, then got up to answer it.

'For you,' she said.

'But . . . is it local?'

'Uh-huh.'

'But no one knows I'm back!'

'Don't they? There was a bit in the paper just this morning.'

'Oh . . . all right.' Ashley got up and took the phone from her. 'Hello?'

'Mrs Lineham? This is Pamela Flint. I'm Mr Reid's secretary, Mr Ross Reid . . .'

Ashley went still.

Pamela continued after a slight hesitation. 'Er . . . Mr Reid has asked me to tell you that he has certain business of a legal nature to discuss with you, and he wondered whether it would be convenient for you to come into his office tomorrow morning?'

Ashley licked her lips, and when she spoke her voice was hoarse, though clipped. 'All right. Tell . . . Mr Reid, I'll be there at ten.' She put the phone down.

Pamela also put the phone down. 'Ten o'clock,' she said to Ross.

'Good,' he replied curtly.

'Unfortunately,' Pamela glanced at the hard set of his mouth and the way his dark eyes were still smouldering, as they had since he'd read the letter from Sydney, 'Mrs Goodman is booked in at ten o'clock to see you about her will. Shall I ring her and see if I can make another appointment?'

'Yes, and cancel everything else tomorrow until lunchtime.' He swung away from her desk, and something about the way he walked into his inner sanctum and slammed the door reminded Pamela acutely of an angry beast on the prowl. And she thought, perhaps it's not all history, because I've seen you arrogant and angry before, but not . . . how to describe it? She sought for the right description . . . dangerous, yes, dark, damning and dangerous, that was it. But there was no doubt he was in a dangerous mood now.

As for Ashley Lineham, she had sounded, in the few words she'd uttered, strained and cold.

For the life of her, Pamela Flint could not suppress a little shiver of morbid anticipation at the prospect of tomorrow's ten o'clock appointment.

Before she went to bed herself, Ashley wandered around the old homestead. Everyone else was asleep, Susie in the main bedroom she herself would be using now, Tasha in her old bedroom which Maggie had maintained exactly as she'd left it five years ago.

But although the property had an air of neglect to the trained eye, the house was in good shape. It was a comfortable, rambling, low-set house with spacious rooms and some lovely old cedar and mahogany furniture, and it was set in a bowl of low hills that provided shelter when the icy winter westerlies were ravaging the New England area of New South Wales. There was an extensive kitchen garden, Maggie's pride and joy, behind the house and leading up the stables and sheds. But there was no formal garden other than shrub and tree-dotted lawn around the house, so that from the wide front veranda there was a vista of sky and space towards a dam that reflected the sky, before the hills rose up.

Four generations of Crawfords had lived on and worked Crawford Downs. Five, if you count me now, Ashley mused as she moved through the

dim, quiet rooms. But then I didn't count, that
was the problem. Why couldn't I have been a
boy? It would have saved . . . so much. It might
have given my poor mother some peace of mind
when she'd discovered she could have no more
children and my father realised the Crawford line
had come to a sonless stop. It could have saved
me . . .

She picked up a silver-framed photo and stared
at the two girls in it bleakly. It had been taken on
the night of her high-school formal dance, and
she and her best friend Bronwen were captured
for all time in their pretty white dresses, their
hair up and their expressions and stances
radiating youthful exuberance and vitality and,
unbeknown to them at the time, innocence.

It was unmistakable now, though, and Ashley
put the frame down with a shaky hand.

She sank down into a wing-backed chair in the
living-room, and her thoughts roamed back over
the last five years. But of course the seeds of
them, the events that had set in train not only the
loss of that innocence and trust but the loss of
even her friends, went back much further. She
sighed and got up restlessly, but there was
nothing to do but go to bed.

Susie was fast asleep in the small bed they'd
moved into the room until she got used to the
house.

Ashley sat on the double bed, brushing her hair
and watching her, and reflecting that it was

always hard to tell how Susie was coping, whereas Tasha was like an open book. Will it work? she wondered, getting up at last and crossing to the dressing-table. Was I . . . naïve to think I could come back, even without what has happened? But it was like a . . . force I couldn't control, especially after Laurie suggested it, and even when I discovered . . .

'Why, oh, why did you do it, Laurie?' she whispered. 'Without even *telling* me?'

Her image in the mirror, her tall, slim figure in a grey silk nightgown that matched her eyes as she stared at it, gave no answer, only reflected subtly the extra air of tension that had overtaken her since she'd found out . . .

CHAPTER TWO

AT FIVE to ten the next morning, Pamela Flint's eye was caught by a flash of maroon, and she glanced up and out of the window to see that it was a maroon Jaguar, reversing into a parking place across the street. She watched the sleek, gleaming car admiringly for a moment, then her eyes narrowed as Ashley Lineham stepped out, locked the door and opened her purse to find change for the parking meter.

Pamela was still staring as Ashley crossed the road towards the office, and thinking that she'd been right—that early promise of beauty had been fulfilled. And as she watched a playful breeze moulded the silky, small-print, predominantly navy and white dress Ashley wore to the long, slender outline of her thigh as she stepped off the central reservation. The breeze also ruffled her long dark hair and, if anything, it settled even more attractively about her oval face.

Not only beautiful, Pamela mused, as she took in the simplicity of Ashley's outfit—the high, sling-back red shoes, the red soft leather clutch-bag and a matching red flower tucked into the lapel of her dress, the cut and style of which accentuated her slim waist and lovely bosom—but utterly elegant. Then she was on her feet as the street door opened with a tinkle of the old-fashioned bell that Ross had kept when he'd taken over from the previous elderly occupants of the rooms.

'Hello,' Ashley said coolly as she advanced across the room, 'I'm . . . why,' she broke off and a smile curved her lips and lit her grey eyes, 'it's Mrs Flint, isn't it? I'm sorry, I didn't recognise the name last night. How are you? And how's Janine? It's been ages . . .' She broke off and bit her lip.

Pamela smiled at her warmly. 'We're all fine, thank you, Ashley. And Janine's given away horses for nursing, believe it or not. She's specialising in midwifery.'

'Oh, is she? What hospital? I'd like to get in touch with her again.'

Pamela told her and added, 'I'm sure she'd be thrilled to hear from——'

She broke off, and they both turned at a sound to see Ross Reid watching them from the doorway of his office. For a long time afterwards, Pamela was to remember the sudden electric air of tension that seemed to pervade the room as Ashley's cool grey gaze met her employer's. Nor did she forget the way they just stared at each other, until a faint tinge of colour stained Ashley's pale cheeks and neck, and she looked away at last.

That was when Pamela stepped into the breach. 'Mrs Lineham, Mr Reid,' she said formally, and returned the dark, sardonic look

Ross flicked her with an unruffled one of her own.

'Thank you, Pam,' he murmured. 'Mrs Lineham and I have met. Come in, Ashley.'

The door closed firmly behind them, leaving Pamela staring at it thoughtfully.

'Why?'

Ashley closed her eyes briefly, then looked up from the letter Ross had tossed on to the desk for her to read. 'I don't know,' she said, barely audibly.

'You must have some idea,' Ross said coldly, coming back from the window where he'd stood with his back to her as she read. He sat down in the leather swivel-chair on the other side of the desk. 'What reasons did he give you?'

'He . . .' Ashley cleared her throat. 'He didn't give me any reasons—he didn't even tell me he was going to do it.'

'He didn't *tell* you?' Ross said, softly but with so much menacing disbelief that she moved defensively. 'Didn't tell you,' he continued, 'that he was going to appoint me as a trustee for *both* his daughters, neither of whom I've laid eyes on? For that matter, I barely knew the man himself . . . you don't honestly expect me to believe that, do you, Ashley? I know you have a certain disregard for the truth, but I never believed you were a fool.'

Ashley stared at her hands and shivered. She'd known this interview would be a nightmare,

known that just to have to face Ross Reid again
would be incredibly hard, but it was exceeding
her expectations. He's changed so little, she
thought, except that those good looks, that
beautiful physique, have translated to a man of
learning and success as if he was born to it. But
then the intelligence was always there, and the
wit—and the fact that he was always a step ahead
of me . . .

'He . . . I think it was an afterthought,' she said
huskily. 'It wasn't included in his main will, it
wasn't even found until a few weeks ago. He had
so many papers, you see. But when they did find
it they . . . insisted it was legal and valid.'

'You tried to . . . contest it?'

'Yes,' Ashley admitted. 'At least, I took advice
on what chance I had of contesting it. He also,'
she paused, 'he also left a letter attached,
outlining his reasons for choosing you.' She
looked up at last and their gazes caught and held.
'He . . . we had discussed what I would do after
he died. He'd known for a long time that his
health was very precarious and . . . and he was in
favour of me coming back to Crawford Downs
with . . . with the girls. He'd also, apparently,
followed your career and approved of it—your
integrity, and not only that—you acted for him
once on a boundary dispute, he said, that had
dragged on for years, but it was your ability that
had finally solved it. And because your practice is
here, he said it was . . . practical.'

'Did he now?' Ross said with a mocking little

smile. 'You're sure he didn't mention that we were once lovers, you and I, Ashley? And that he was contemplating handing you back to me?'

'I . . .'

'*Used* but still beautiful?'

'Ross . . .'

'He did know about us, didn't he, Ashley? Did he feel . . . cheated on your wedding night? I often wondered if you had to explain why you weren't a virgin.'

Ashley stared at him, then she stood up in one fluid movement, her grey eyes bright with anger. 'I knew this would be impossible,' she said in a low, uneven voice. 'So—goodbye, Ross. Any further dealings will have to be through *my* solicitor.'

He caught her at the door. 'Oh, no, you don't,' he said through his teeth, his hands hard on her upper arms. 'There are some answers I intend getting—and if you care to recall, I was always stronger than you.'

'Let me go,' she said tightly.

But he only smiled slightly and pulled her into his arms.

'Ross . . .' She said his name on a breath.

'Do you ever think of those days, Ashley?' he drawled. 'The days when you thought you could outshoot, outride, outdo any man? The days when you were seventeen going on eighteen, and you hated yourself not only because you couldn't outdo me, but also because you found yourself wondering what it would be like to be kissed, held, made love to? Like this . . .'

She made an inarticulate little sound and her face was paper pale as she stared up into his mocking dark eyes, and to her horror her body was flooded with the memories of the burgeoning excitement mingled with the mental confusion Ross had aroused in her once. It all came flooding back—her anger and bewilderment because she'd not known how to handle it then, had seen it as some sort of weakness for a time and, continually and foolishly, tested herself against him. One whole long, hot summer vacation she'd pitted herself against him, she remembered, to his wry, silent amusement. And then, when it had ended and he was gone, she was left in a fever of impatience for the next vacation . . . and left with the horrifying suspicion that one word, one look from him would have totally melted her spurious opposition.

But even worse than the memories, as he held her against him, her arms pinned to her sides, the feel of his hands on her back and waist, the feel of her breasts against him, slightly crushed, was the suspicion now that if he did kiss her, she would be unable to still her response . . .

He didn't. After a moment more that seemed like an eternity, he released her and stood back, but indicated the chair she'd left.

Ashley drew a ragged breath, then steeled herself and sat down again.

'Did he know about us?' he asked quietly, in a voice devoid of all inflection.

'No. He knew . . . there was someone, but I never told him who.'

'So you think,' he gestured at the letter on the desk, 'this is all an incredible coincidence?'

'I don't know what else to think.'

He was silent, staring at her bent head, the way her hair hid her face, the twisted grace of the way she was sitting half turned away from him. Then she looked up suddenly. 'Ross, I know what you must think of me.' She hesitated and gripped the arm of the chair so that her knuckles turned white. 'There is one way out of this.'

He raised an eyebrow.

'If . . . if you refused to accept the trusteeship, someone else would be appointed.'

'Is that what you want me to do?'

'I . . . I thought it would be what you would want to do,' she said very quietly.

'Well, that's unfortunate,' he replied after a time. 'Because I've decided to accept . . . Laurie Lineham's faith in my ability and integrity, Ashley. So—it's Saturday tomorrow. I think you'd better invite me out to Crawford Downs for lunch, to . . . meet these two girls I'm so ironically entrusted with. Don't you?'

It was Ashley's turn to be silent, painfully so, until she said, 'Is there nothing I can do to make you change your mind?'

He sat back in his chair, thoughtfully. 'Nothing I can think of at present. Tell me,' his dark gaze flickered over her leisurely and indifferently, 'did you ever have any regrets about throwing me over for Laurence Lineham?'

'Did I do that?' she said huskily, returning his gaze steadily, although her heart was beating heavily. '*You* told me marriage didn't figure in your plans then.'

'That was before we slept together,' he murmured. 'And then you virtually went straight from my arms to his bed.'

They stared at each other until she looked away from the cynical contempt in his eyes, and stood up.

'No, no regrets,' she whispered, and turned to the door. 'Goodbye, Ross.'

'Goodbye, Ashley—until tomorrow, that is. I'll be out about twelve. Will that be convenient for you?'

'Fine.' She glanced at him expressionlessly over her shoulder, then let herself out quietly.

It wasn't until after dinner, and Ashley and Maggie were doing the dishes while Natasha bathed Susie, that Maggie said, 'Didn't go too good, I gather.'

'No.'

'Want to talk about it?'

'There's not a lot to say,' Ashley replied wearily. 'I didn't . . . really expect that he would forgive or forget easily.'

'Hmm.' Maggie put a saucepan down with some force. 'I know who to blame, even if he doesn't!'

'Mag,' Ashley said with a faint smile, 'you

know you like Ross, you always did. Don't let this change it. Anyway, for everyone's sake, I'd like us to be as normal as possible tomorrow.'

Maggie snorted. 'Normal? When I *think* . . .'

'Please don't . . .' Ashley said tensely.

Maggie stood with her arms akimbo, then her lined old face softened. 'All right, lovey,' she said gruffly. 'Trust your old Mag!'

'This man, our trustee,' Tasha said over breakfast the next morning, 'the one who's coming to lunch, what's he like? Will he be stingy over pocket money? And what will he think about my show-jumping ambitions?'

It was Maggie who replied. 'Seeing as how he rode and jumped a horse better than anyone I knew, even your stepmama, if I may say so, and that's saying *something*, he'll probably be quite interested.'

Tasha's blue eyes brightened. 'Maybe that's why Daddy chose him. What a pity Cornflower isn't arriving until Monday!' Cornflower was her pony. 'Ash, can I ask him to come back and see me jump her?'

Ashley looked up from the pancake she was buttering for Susan. 'I expect he's pretty busy,' she said.

'Well, I presume he's getting paid for his services,' Tasha said with a tilt of her chin that reminded Ashley acutely of Tasha's father.

'Dear me,' Maggie observed, 'I don't think Ross will be impressed by that attitude.'

For a moment Tasha looked haughtier, then her almost irrepressible good humour took over and she giggled. 'You're right. That's what my last governess used to say. "Just because you're Natasha Lineham, it doesn't mean to say you can get all hoity-toity with me!" I'll be very nice to him, Ash,' she promised.

'Does he like puppies?' Susan enquired. 'I asked Father Christmas for a puppy, but he didn't get me one. Should I ask him?'

'Darling,' Ashley said, 'we explained why you couldn't have a puppy before, but I guess there's no reason not to now—I'll see about it. Incidentally, girls, we don't have to kowtow to him, you know. His job is merely to make sure your affairs are handled properly. It's my job to make the day-to-day decisions.'

'My affairs,' Tasha said dreamily. 'That has a lovely sound to it. It makes me feel really important!'

'Important or not,' Maggie said, 'Ashley assures me your father wanted you to have a good, plain upbringing. And in this house that means helping with the dishes.'

Susan slipped off her chair. 'Can I help you feed the chickens, Maggie?' she asked shyly.

'Not only that, but we can make that your job.' Maggie said, taking her by the hand and leading her out on to the back porch.

Ashley watched them go.

'Susie's made a friend!' Tasha crowed.

Ashley smiled with a tinge of relief. 'Yes.'

'So,' Ross turned from Ashley, 'I guess we have here Miss Susan and Miss Natasha Lineham. How do you do? I'm Ross Reid.' He offered his hand gravely to Tasha first.

Tasha took it, but her eyes were wide and she said, 'Gosh! I expected some dried-up old fuddy-duddy, even if you did jump horses once!'

'Tasha——' Ashley murmured.

'But I did! I'm so sorry. Wow!'

Ross laughed. 'Do you . . . like to jump horses by any chance, Tasha?' he asked.

'Do I ever? Which is something I wanted to talk to you about but,' she caught Ashley's eye, 'well, over lunch, maybe. This is Susie. She's a bit shy,' she added, as Susan, who was clutching Ashley's hand, turned her face away embarrassedly.

'It's all still a bit strange,' Ashley said quietly.

'Of course.' His dark eyes lingered on Susan, though, until she looked up at him at last.

'Do you like horses as well, Susie?' he asked.

'I like puppies,' she said breathlessly, then with a determination that took both Ashley and Tasha by surprise she added, 'Can I talk to you 'bout *that* at lunch?'

He raised an eyebrow, but said seriously, 'With pleasure. It so happens I know where there are some puppies to be had . . . if your mother approves.'

'Well, there you are, Ross!' Maggie said,

coming out on to the veranda. 'It's been a long time since you used to raid my kitchen and try to chat me up!'

'Maggie! If I ever did, it was because you certainly knew the way to a man's heart, as well as being charming and intelligent . . .'

'Now, now, Ross Reid,' Maggie warned, but she was laughing, 'none of your nonsense! Come in and have lunch.'

Susan, again to everyone's surprise, elected to leave Ashley's side and walk in with Ross.

'I call that puppy love if ever I saw it!' Tasha whispered into Ashley's ear as they followed. 'But why didn't you warn me? He's gorgeous—what wouldn't I give to have him chat me up!'

'Certainly two carrot-tops,' Ross said. Laurence left his mark.'

They were alone on the veranda with their coffee, sheltered from the sun but with the heady scents of an almost perfect summer's day wafting past. Like herself, Ross wore jeans, but his were grey, and he wore a black polo shirt open at the throat, whereas her jeans were blue and she wore a white blouse and she'd tied her hair back in the nape of her neck. It was Maggie's organisation that had achieved their being alone together, but he had gone out of his way to make lunch as pleasant as possible; they all had, Ashley thought. I guess the gloves will be off again now we're alone, though . . . She shivered slightly.

Ross must have noticed, because he said, 'What is it?'

'Nothing. What do you think of them—apart from their red hair?'

'I think . . . Susie looks more like you than anyone.'

'So does Maggie.'

'Don't you?'

Ashley shrugged. 'It's hard to see yourself in someone else. And with the red hair . . .'

'Yes,' he said slowly. 'As for the other one,' he grinned, 'she's a honey and quite a handful, I imagine.'

'She is a honey,' Ashley said gratefully. 'I'm very fond of her.'

'That's fortunate, isn't it? That she should have you, I mean.'

'Well, it is—her closest other living relative is her stepbrother, Laurie's son by his first wife.'

'Apart from Susan, you mean.'

'Well, yes, of course, but . . . I meant as far as someone to take care of her goes. He's only nineteen, and his mother is not . . . well-disposed towards . . .' She hesitated.

'Succeeding wives and their offspring?' Ross supplied drily.

'No . . .'

'All the same, he was left the larger part of his father's fortune.'

Ashley looked across at him. 'How . . .?'

'I've been doing my homework. Oh, he was generous enough to his daughters, but one thing that surprised me was how little he left you, relatively.'

'He . . .' Ashley sipped her coffee and started again. 'I didn't want his fortune. And that . . . relatively little is all I need.'

'Oh?'

'Yes, Ross,' she said quietly. 'Because I intend to get Crawford Downs on its feet again and paying my way.'

'That's a big undertaking, Ashley,' he said softly.

'It's also a challenge I . . . need.'

'Then I wish you well,' he said abruptly.

'Thanks.'

'Why did you shiver earlier?'

Ashley looked away. 'Did I?'

'You looked as if someone was walking over your grave.'

'I thought, once we were alone you might . . .' She stopped and bit her lip.

'I might return to the attack?' he queried.

'Ross . . .'

'I might still,' he murmured. 'Tell me, is it of any interest to you how I've spent the last five years?'

'I . . . I know that. Maggie kept me updated. Congratulations, you've done marvellously well,' she said awkwardly.

'Thank you. All I need now, so some people tell me, is a wife.'

'Is . . . is there someone?' Ashley asked.

'Look at me, Ash,' he commanded coldly. 'At

least have the decency to do that, if you're at all interested.'

She took a breath, then reluctantly raised her grey eyes to his. 'There's no one special,' he said after a time. 'I seem to have acquired a certain cynicism towards women. Do you remember,' he went on softly, 'the summer you turned nineteen?'

Ashley put her cup down carefully. 'I *knew*,' she said tautly, 'you decided to accept the trusteeship only so that you could go on . . . taunting me and humiliating me.'

He laughed quietly. 'As a matter of fact, that opportunity would have presented itself to me anyway. Did you not take that into consideration when you decided to come back?'

'Yes,' she said tightly. 'Oh, yes.'

'But you came all the same.'

'This is my home. I spent half my life trying to convince my father I *could* run it, that I needn't be such a disappointment to him because I wasn't a son, that it meant as much to me as it did to him.'

'Yet you left it with barely a backward glance once,' he murmured.

'Ross,' she said coldly and proudly, 'I did so for reasons of my own. I also came back for reasons of my own, and I plan to stay.'

He lifted an ironic eyebrow at her. 'In other words, Ross Reid,' he drawled, 'do your damnedest.'

'In a word—yes.'

'You always were . . . proud, Ashley,' he said softly, 'but it might not have been wise to throw down the gauntlet like that. Because I intend to . . . Did you love him—as you thought you loved me?'

Ashley stared at him.

'Or did I, unwittingly, unlock a need within you that . . .'

'You bastard,' she whispered.

'Well, what am I supposed to think?' he countered. 'In the absense of one word of explanation, what would you think? Do you know what happened after you left? Your father threatened me with a shotgun if I dared set foot on the place again, and if I so much as tried to get in touch with you. He also threatened to have me run out of town . . . a colourful, meaningless threat, but none the less, in the heat of the moment he added that I wasn't good enough for you, never would be and you *knew* it, otherwise you wouldn't have married Laurence Lineham.'

Ashley put a hand to her mouth.

'Which in fact made sense, Ashley,' he continued. 'At least, it was the only sense I could make of it. Why would you . . . unless you'd inherited your father's incredible and outdated sense of *noblesse oblige*? Employees are fair game for a fling, but you draw the line at marrying them. Once upon a time, you yourself used to go out of your way to put me in my place, Ashley,' he said mockingly.

Ashley closed her eyes and her shoulders sagged.

'Incidentally,' she heard him say dispassionately,

and she tensed, 'another codicil to your husband's will has been found.'

Ashley's lashes flew up and she stared at him incredulously. 'What . . . what this time?' she demanded hoarsely. 'And how do you know?'

'I know because I'm implicated again, and his Sydney solicitors contacted me yesterday afternoon. They also sent the papers up by special courier. Two sets—one for you, one for me.' He reached into the back pocket of his jeans and withdrew an envelope which he handed to her.

Ashley took it fearfully and opened it with fumbling fingers. And her eyes dilated as she read. 'I don't believe it,' she whispered at last. 'I . . .'

'I would if I were you,' Ross drawled. 'There's no mistake.'

'But this means . . .' The words stuck in Ashley's throat and she couldn't go on.

'It means,' he said casually, 'that any money of your inheritance from him that you intend to put into Crawford Downs, you may only do so in consultation with me. It's a fairly sensible condition.'

'Forgive me, but as things stand,' Ashley said through her teeth, 'it's a diabolical condition! In any case, it's a typically *male* one. *Oh* . . .' And, in a gesture of anger and despair, she crumpled the document into a ball. Ross merely watched her steadily and in a totally unmoved manner.

Ashley set her jaw, then started to speak again, but she heard footsteps and Susie came round the corner of the veranda with a book in her hands.

She started to say something once more, but Susie took the book to Ross and laid it on his knee. 'This is my book of puppies,' she said to him gravely. 'Would you like to see it?'

All the indifference was wiped from his expression, Ashley saw, as he grinned and ruffled Susie's red hair, saying, 'Indeed I would.' Then he glanced at Ashley. 'How *do* you feel about a puppy? Because I've got the feeling we're under siege, and I happen to know of a litter of Border Collie pups almost ready to leave their mother.'

'I . . . thank you,' Ashley said a little helplessly.

'What an absolute dreamboat!' Tasha enthused as they all waved Ross off later. 'And he said he would like to see Cornflower when he brings the puppy. If only I were older,' she added sadly. 'How old is he, anyway?'

'Never you mind, young lady,' Maggie said, but with a grin.

'Well, it can work, Maggie,' Tasha replied. 'Daddy was a lot older than Ashley.'

'Ashley wasn't barely fifteen at the time,' Maggie retorted, then her grin faded as she glanced at Ashley. 'All right, inside, you lot,' she commanded. 'Saturday afternoon is hairwash time around these parts!'

Ashley smiled mechanically, remembering how inflexible Maggie's routines were, and how many Saturday afternoons she'd spent a portion of sitting in the sun drying her hair. 'I'll leave you to it,' she murmured. 'I've got a few things to look at.'

*   *   *

'What's that?' Maggie enquired as Ashley sat at the dining-room table, making notes, after dinner. The girls were watching television.

'A . . . plan of procedure,' Ashley replied. 'Where to start, in other words, and I think the two top priorities are new staff and new fences. Then I intend to build up the flock . . . do you know, Mag, wool is coming back into its own to an extent?'

'So I hear say. You're lucky we've had a few good seasons, Ashley. A couple of years back, what with hardly any rain, there was barely a blade of grass in some paddocks.'

'That's another thing,' Ashley made a note, 'I thought of putting a dam in Four Mile paddock. There's a natural depression in the west corner of it which we can enlarge. Staff,' she said with a sigh, throwing down her pen, 'that's not going to be so easy.'

'All the good ones drifted away after your father died,' Maggie commented. 'And without someone to boss them around . . .' She shrugged.

'I know. I think I'd like a couple. I mean, a married couple to start with.'

'Sensible! On the other hand, the manager's cottage is in a right bad state.'

Ashley picked up her pen wearily and wrote, 'Inspect Cottage'. 'Actually,' she murmured, 'I should put that at the top of the list, because without a good right-hand man I'm virtually hamstrung, and without somewhere decent for his wife to live so she can keep him happy because she's happy herself, I'm wasting my time!'

'How will you go about getting this couple?' Maggie asked.

'I think,' Ashley said slowly, 'I'll go through a stock and station agency first. They can do the preliminary interviews and . . . the sorting the wheat from the chaff. Then I'll make the final decision. I might have to go down to Sydney for a couple of days, but I don't think the girls will mind staying with you, Mag.'

Maggie smiled. 'The little one is opening up day by day. She's a quiet little thing, isn't she? Took to Ross, though.'

'So did Tasha,' Ashley said wryly.

'Mmm. Awkward age,' Maggie said. 'But she's mad enough about horses for it not to be too great a problem yet. All the same, in her next school holidays, we'll have to do something about making her friends. You . . . had things out with yourself this afternoon? After he left, I mean.'

Ashley smiled. 'You don't miss a thing, Maggie. Yes, I did. I'm fine.'

Maggie shot her a piercing glance, but said only, 'If you say so.'

Ashley hesitated, then she said with a gesture to her pad, 'Of course, I have to get Ross's approval for all this. That . . . was the other thing he came out to tell me.'

Maggie pursed her lips. 'Might not be a bad idea.'

Ashley glanced at her expressively.

'Well,' Maggie said stubbornly, 'he of all people should know Crawford Downs like the back of his hand '

Ashley was about to reply, but once again Susie intervened.

She came into the room and climbed on to Ashley's lap. 'Tired, darling?' Ashley asked.

Susie hesitated. 'Only if you'll read me a story in bed.'

'You're becoming quite a little wheeler-dealer! All right.'

'Liked that man,' Susie said sleepily after her story and as Ashley was tucking her in.

'Good . . . 'Night, baby.' Ashley kissed her smooth, soft little cheek.

Ross returned the following week with a black and white puppy from which Susie instantly became inseparable.

'I guess she misses her father,' he said to Ashley, watching Susie solemnly fixing up a bed in an old basket for the wobbly little creature.

'We all do,' Ashley replied quietly.

'Of course,' he said, but, when Ashley glanced at him to see if he was being sardonic, he was only still watching Susie thoughtfully.

'Have you thought,' he said then, 'that this could be a strangely isolated life for her and Tasha? With no male influence?'

'Yes, I had thought of that. I can't just manufacture some male relatives, though.'

'Just as well they have me, then,' he said blandly.

'You have a point,' Ashley murmured.

He raised an eyebrow and studied her thoughtfully. 'I see,' he said at last.

They were standing side by side on the lawn below the veranda, and it was another perfect summer's day, a Sunday this time. Faithful to another of Maggie's inflexible routines, they had all dressed up and gone to church—Ashley had been surprised and warmed by the number of people who had come to welcome her back—then they'd come home to have a roast dinner. Ashley still wore a pale blue and grey striped shirt-dress with a grey leather belt and matching grey, medium-heeled shoes—suitable Sunday attire according to Maggie's lights, although Susie and Tasha had been allowed to change. Ross was again in his black shirt and grey jeans.

Ashley stirred and slid her hands into her skirt pockets. 'What do you see?'

'You've changed your position to a policy of non-confrontation,' he said drily.

She smiled faintly and turned to look at him. 'Violence begets violence, they say. I beg to differ, however. *Yours* was the confrontation policy.'

'Oh, I can play a cat and mouse game, too,' he said.

'Ross,' she said wearily, 'there is no game, there is no contest—don't you see, this is ridiculous?'

He didn't answer her for a long time, just studied her meditatively until she looked away from those probing dark eyes, from everything about him that had always tormented her from the time she'd first laid eyes on him.

'Don't,' he said quietly, capturing her chin.

'You're right—we'll call a truce here because of . . . because I don't care to carry this kind of war on in front of children. But there'll be other times, other places, Ashley. I give you fair warning.' He released her chin and his dark gaze dropped fleetingly to her breasts beneath the crisp blue and grey cotton.

'This war,' she said huskily, 'what is to be won?'

He considered. 'My peace of mind, perhaps,' he said at last.

'I thought you had me . . . taped, as a mercenary bitch with delusions of grandeur, not to mention nymphomaniac tendencies.'

'My, my, your eyes have lost none of their fire when you're in a temper, Ashley,' he remarked. 'You said it,' he added.

'I'm also not averse to . . . picking up a gauntlet,' she countered, 'in my own way—there'll only be business contacts between us from now on, Ross. It seems that I can't avoid, but that's all. In fact I've got some . . . ideas to show you, if you have the time.'

'Sure.' He smiled, but it didn't reach his eyes, and his parting shot just as Tasha came cantering around the house on Cornflower was the last thing Ashley expected—and perhaps the worst, or best, he could have chosen.

'At least I don't have to live here with the memories,' he murmured.

CHAPTER THREE

'DAMN him,' Ashley muttered to herself a couple of days later. She wiped the sweat off her face and pulled her blouse out of her jeans.

She'd continued her thorough inspection of the property on foot and on horseback, making mental notes which she added to her written notes each night. But everywhere she went, or so it seemed, the memories lurked, catching her unawares as now . . .

This time it was a small spinney at the corner of four paddocks, close enough to the dam near the homestead to have a permanent underground water-pipe from it connected to several drinking troughs. It wasn't a perfect system. The depth of the water in the troughs, when down to a certain level, was supposed to activate an old-fashioned system of levers and floats that turned the water on from the pipes and then turned it off again before it overflowed. Sheep were adept, however, at interfering with it, and it frequently played up and overflowed of its own accord—with two results. It had to be checked often, and over the years a pleasantly lush, cool and leafy dell had grown up around it, particularly in the corner of the paddock where there wasn't a trough, and consequently no sheep to regularly trample and eat the undergrowth.

Ashley was in an opposite paddock, but she tied her horse to a tree so that it could drink from a trough, and with an exasperated sigh she climbed the fence.

'If you can't shut them out of your mind, maybe you should take them out and look them in the face,' she whispered, as she glanced around and then sank down to sit on the grass with her back against a tree.

The summer I turned nineteen, she thought. Things changed that summer, didn't they? I stopped playing the daughter of the manor and had the sense not to indulge in any more useless contests.

And Ross played along, as he always had. With that silent, wry amusement at first, but it lessened gradually, with no *sign* otherwise that he was aware of how he affected me, and had been affecting me since he was first engaged as a jackeroo during his summer vacations when I was only sixteen.

'Was I so proud and determined to put him in his place even then?' she asked herself as she unseeingly plucked a blade of grass and twisted the slender, springy stem around her fingers. She closed her eyes and laid her head back against the tree.

The answer, of course, was yes, she mused. For a variety of reasons. My father was a proud, forceful man and I grew up with some of his convictions instilled in me—and not all of them were bad. He did believe in giving everything you did your all, he did teach me to be independent and, I guess, reserved. Added to that, *I* was trying to prove I was as good as any man a lot of the time. Then Ross came . . .

She opened her eyes and stared upwards at the leafy canopy above, remembering as if it was yesterday . . .

'Who the hell is that?' she asked, looking out of the kitchen window as she sat at the kitchen table drinking tea and eating Maggie's gingerbread, still dressed in her school uniform because she'd only just arrived home at the end of term.

'Tut, tut,' Maggie said. 'Wouldn't have thought that expensive school would teach you to swear.'

Ashley slanted her a grin, then looked out of the window again, only to rise with a frown. 'Well, who the hell is he? And who gave him permission to ride *my* horse?' she demanded.

'Your father,' Maggie said calmly. 'And his name is Ross Reid. He's lived with the Donoghues outside Tamworth since he was ten as a foster child, he's studying law at Armidale now and working through his holidays to pay his way. Your father gave him permission to ride your horse because she was getting fat and lazy, he said.'

'Well, I'm here now, so I'll be exercising her myself, and what's more I'll tell him so!' She buttered herself another piece of gingerbread and went into her bedroom with it, where she changed quickly into jeans and riding-boots, although she didn't bother to take her hair out of its pigtail.

'Ashley, it's not his fault!' Maggie said as Ashley passed through the kitchen again on her way to the stables.

'Then he won't mind finding himself something else to ride when I explain who I am,' Ashley said coolly over her shoulder.

But Ross Reid, seen at close quarters as he hosed Ashley's horse down, was something of a revelation. His jeans were faded and patched, his boots scuffed and his khaki shirt had had the sleeves cut out of it. None of that in any way diminished the lean, tall strength and grace of his body, nor did the accumulated sweat and grime of a hard day's work hide his dark, vital good looks.

'Well,' he said, looking up over the horse's back straight into Ashley's annoyed but wavering into surprise, grey gaze, 'Good day. And who might you be?'

The surprise faded from Ashley's eyes, to be replaced by reserve, added to the annoyance, 'I'm Ashley Crawford,' she said stiffly, 'and this is my horse.'

Ross Reid turned the hose off. 'My apologies, ma'am,' he drawled. 'Perhaps your father didn't explain to you that he asked me to exercise her for you?'

Ashley bit her lip. 'Thank you,' she muttered.

'But now I'm home, I can do it.' It came out sounding churlish and ungracious, but after a moment of allowing his dark eyes to roam over her Ross merely looked amused.

He also unclipped the horse and handed her the lead, saying, 'There you go, then. She's a beauty.' And with a pat on her neck, to which the mare responded with an affectionate nuzzle of his hand, he turned away and walked off without a backward glance.

And that, Ashley mused nearly ten years later, set the scene. For the whole of that summer I was tongue-tied and surly, but whenever I thought of boys, mingled with them in the holidays or at school socials, I always found myself thinking of Ross, who was the best-looking of them and, besides that, a man, and the least interested. In fact, when he wasn't being polite, he simply ignored me. It was the next summer I . . . went to war. Why? So that he couldn't ignore me any more? Because I was sub-consciously testing my feminine powers? Because I hated the way he only had to look at me sometimes to make me aware of my body . . . because of the secret thoughts I had about the strength and . . . beauty of his body?

Yes, all that, she reflected, and more. Because he saw through my sometimes pitiful little ploys designed to make him at least acknowledge I was a girl, a woman, even if only for the pleasure of being able to slap him down. If there was ever a thoroughly mixed-up girl, it was me—determined to be as good as a man, dying to be treated like a desirable woman, *knowing* my father would sack him on the spot if he ever stepped over the line, and unable even to imagine what he'd do to me if he ever thought I was encouraging Ross . . .

And spending half my life in miserable jealousy over the girls he did sometimes take out. She sighed and closed her eyes again. Then there was my nineteenth—no, twentieth summer, the summer I got to know him. The summer he allowed me close enough to talk to me. Sometimes here, in the spinney . . . This is where he told me about the orphanage his unmarried mother put him in because she'd refused to give him up for adoption, only to find later that she couldn't support him. Told me unemotionally about his foster parents, who were good to him, and how it was through them he'd been inspired to make something of his life, in spite of its rather dismal beginning. He told me about law school, told me about his dreams and ambitions, talked to me properly, as if I was an adult, for the first time. And I couldn't get enough of it, although by then I had the sense to . . . keep certain things to myself—well, the sense to keep my emotions under control and out of sight. I thought. Perhaps I was kidding myself, because he did also let it slip that marriage didn't figure in his plans for a long time. But that was a gentle, kind summer, even if I knew, or thought, that he didn't reciprocate the turbulent emotions I'd felt for so long. That was the summer I began to appreciate how much there was to Ross, the summer I fell in

love as opposed to an adolescent crush . . . Oh,
hell, she scrambled up and brushed herself off
convulsively, why did I ever think it would help
to . . . remember? The best, the only thing to do,
is go on blanking the memories out as best I
can!

Maggie took one glance at her distraught face
when she arrived back at the house, and an
unusually determined look even for Maggie lit
her old blue eyes.

'Sit down,' she commanded, and indicated the
kitchen-table.

Ashley ignored the command and said,
'Where's Susie?'

'Up at the stables with Tasha. Will you sit
down, Ashley Crawford, or do I have to make
you?'

Ashley shrugged and finally complied. 'Why?'

'Because I'm telling you to,' Maggie said
grimly. 'And don't you dare move—I'll be back in
a tick.'

She was, too, with a cut-glass decanter in one
hand and a crystal glass in the other. She splashed
a generous tot of brandy into the glass and
handed it to Ashley. 'Drink some first, then you
can start talking.'

'Mag . . .'

'Ashley, what you're doing to yourself is
helping no one, least of all *you*. You *need* to talk
about it to someone, you can't bottle it all up
inside you for ever, and I'm as good as anyone—

better than anyone, probably! So get started, girl.'

'I . . . where would you like me to start?' Ashley said bitterly.

'You can start by telling me why you married Laurence Lineham, when you felt the way you did about Ross . . .'

'You know why I married him, Maggie!'

Maggie snorted and reached across for a plain tumbler, into which she poured herself some brandy. 'If I know, it's not from anyone telling me in so many words, miss!'

Ashley stared at her, then sighed and looked away. 'I couldn't talk about it . . . to anyone at the time,' she said, barely audibly.

'There's an old saying—better late than never.'

Ashley sipped some brandy. 'Well, you probably guessed that Dad . . . was in financial trouble.'

'He was mighty close about it, but yes, I did,' Maggie conceded.

'Well, it was so serious, the banks were threatening to foreclose on him, partly because of his age and the fact that there was no one to carry on. No sons, at least,' Ashley said bleakly. 'Oh, to give him credit it wasn't all his fault—you know what it's like, Maggie, a few bad seasons, a further drop in wool prices, but all the same, he never really believed synthetics would make such an impression on the market for so long.'

'So many of them didn't,' Maggie murmured. 'Go on.'

Ashley stared at nothing in particular. 'It was at that time that Laurie . . . well, he swore to the day he died that he saw me at the races one day and . . . fell in love with me. I,' Ashley swallowed, 'was barely even aware of his existence, and when he started to make it obvious he was interested, I was very cool. Laurie,' she raised her eyes to Maggie's, 'always maintained his red hair was the outward manifestation of an ungovernable nature, and he then . . . set out to buy me. Dad,' she said huskily, 'as it happened, was only too happy to sell rather than face the prospect of going bankrupt.'

It was Maggie's turn to sigh. 'Don't I know it?' she said sadly. 'He was one of those kind of men women didn't mean much to. He made your poor sainted mother's life a misery, then yours. But still——'

'Maggie,' Ashley broke in urgently, 'all my life I felt guilty because I wasn't the son he'd so desperately wanted. And heaven help me, in the end, one of the reasons I did it was . . . in repayment for all the disappointment he'd suffered, all he'd done for me. I thought—there'll be no more guilt now, I've paid my debts!'

Maggie stared at the tears streaming down Ashley's cheeks, and she said gently, 'Drink some more brandy, love.' Then, 'Tell me about Mr Lineham now. You know, I always had the feeling men would do crazy things over you.'

Ashley sniffed and wiped her nose with the back of her hand, and finally managed a watery smile. 'He . . . I hated him at first.' She closed her eyes and laid her head back. 'But he changed,' she said after a long time. 'He said, when he was recovering from the stroke, that there's something about discovering you're not immortal that makes you stop and think. He . . . we ended up good friends. Maggie,' she lifted her head, 'what would you have done in my place?'

Maggie was silent for a long time. 'I don't know,' she said at last, 'but what matters is that you did what you saw as your duty, and that I admire you for, Ashley.'

'Ross . . .' Ashley stopped.

'Go on.'

'I think you . . . guessed what I did . . . I did about Ross,' Ashley whispered, and their gazes caught and held.

Maggie nodded after a time.

'I shouldn't have done that.'

'Maybe not.'

'He'll never forgive me.'

Maggie considered. 'Only time will tell that,' she said thoughtfully.

'Time won't change anything,' Ashley said very quietly, and she drained the rest of her brandy. 'All the same, thank you for saying what you did. You can tell yourself . . . these things about duty and so on, but sometimes it helps to hear someone else say them.' And she put out a hand and laid it over Maggie's hand on the table, and they sat like that in a curiously peaceful silence for a time.

*　　　*　　　*

It was later that day that Ashley received and made several phone calls, and she said over dinner, 'Mag, the preliminary interviews for a manager have been done, and they've got a short-list for me to interview. Two in Tamworth and two in Sydney. I've got a few other business matters to attend to in Sydney, so I'll be away for three days, probably. Should I take the girls?'

'Can I bring Georgie?' Susie enquired. The Border Collie pup now rejoiced in that name.

'Darling, no,' Ashley said.

'Then I'll stay with Maggie,' Susie replied placidly.

'Tasha?'

'You may not recall, because you've become a bit absent-minded these days, if I may say so, Ash,' Tasha remarked with a twinkle in her eye, 'but Susie and I have been invited to a Young Christian Society barbecue. It will be my debut into society, and I could become a social outcast if I miss it.'

'Society,' Maggie snorted.

'Dear Maggie,' Tasha said gravely, 'if this is to be my home . . .'

'I'm not disputing that—only the high-flown way you put things, miss!' Maggie retorted. 'And I'll be there as one of the chaperones, so there'll be no carrying on as they do in *society*!' She snorted again.

'I take it you're happy to stay, Tasha,' Ashley said with a grin.

'I sure am!'

'Good. Incidentally,' Ashley added to Maggie as the girls went off to watch television, 'I bumped into Bob Mulhall in town yesterday and I offered him his old job back. He's moving into the flat above the stables tomorrow.' She glanced at Maggie through her lashes.

'You did what?' Maggie demanded grimly.

Ashley smiled slightly and said gently, 'Maggie, since I turfed that useless, drunken so-called foreman out, there's not been a man on the property.'

'You call doddery old Bob Mulhall a man?'

'Now, Mag, that's being extremely unkind,' Ashley protested. 'I know you two had your differences over the years, and I know Bob is getting on a bit, but he actually looked very fit to me, and we *need* someone for maintenance jobs about the house, for the lawn and the stables, for protection, if you like . . .'

'I don't . . .'

'And he was always very loyal and a hard worker . . .'

'Stubborn as an old mule . . .'

'And just think,' Ashley said softly, 'how you'll enjoy having someone to spar with again.'

Maggie had opened her mouth, but she closed it and looked mortally offended for a moment. Then a reluctant smile lit her blue eyes, only to be banished as she said tartly, 'I suppose he's bringing those two kelpie dogs of his to bury their bones all over my vegetable garden. Ha! Have you thought what kind of mincemeat they might make of the little one's pup?'

'I discussed that with Bob,' Ashley said gravely. 'They are very well-trained guard dogs, by the way, which means I won't worry about you when I'm away, and Bob reckons he can properly introduce them to Georgie and ensure they don't tear him apart. If you remember, Bob was always marvellous with animals—and children.'

'Any other of his praises you'd like to sing to me, Ashley Crawford?' Maggie asked. 'Maybe you even consider me superfluous!'

'Not at all, Maggie. I don't know what I'd do without you,' Ashley said simply, and hugged the old lady.

'Dear, oh, dear,' Maggie remarked a moment later, dabbing at her eyes with the corner of her apron, 'I must be getting soft in my old age.'

'Oh, no, not you, Mag,' Ashley teased.

But as she got ready for bed later it was in an entirely sober mood, as she thought of what she'd not told Maggie. That, for example, one of the earlier phone calls had been from Ross . . . A businesslike communication on her plans for Crawford Downs, most of which he endorsed, although two he disagreed with entirely, and to her irritation she'd been unable to fault his logic. He'd then asked her about the staff she meant to employ, and she'd told him about the upcoming interviews in Tamworth and Sydney, whereupon he'd told her he was due in Sydney himself. He'd planned to fly down, but if she was driving he would accompany her and be able to sit in on the Tamworth ones as well . . .

The sheer unexpectedness of it had robbed her of words, then what he'd said next had goaded her into accepting.

She thought of them again as she lay in bed, staring into the darkness.

He'd said softly, his voice down the line laced with amusement. 'A perfect opportunity for you to prove how . . . businesslike you can be, Ash, if you can. That is the state of the game between us now, isn't it?'

She bit her lip and turned her cheek to the pillow.

'You drive well,' Ross said casually.

'Thank you,' Ashley replied coolly as she steered the maroon Jaguar down the New England highway away from Tamworth and towards Sydney, and as she concentrated on not only her driving but also erecting a wall of indifference around her. Indifference to Ross, who was sitting only inches from her, wearing a blue and white checked shirt and fawn denim trousers with desert boots; indifference to the way his dark eyes had flicked over her own attire which consisted of a taupe, full cotton skirt, crisp white blouse, a wide, soft jade leather belt that emphasised her slender waist and a matching jade ribbon confining her hair, brown leather pumps and shoulder-bag. Indifference to the mocking little salute in his eyes that had told her he approved. And last but not least, indifference to the way he had handled the two interviews almost as if she hadn't been there.

'You didn't,' he said, lowering his window a couple of inches to let out a fly that had evidently and cunningly decided to accompany them, 'really want to employ either of those two blokes, did you, Ashley?'

She raised her eyebrows. 'No. I don't think they would have been at all suitable.'

'Good. Then you didn't mind me giving them short shrift. As a matter of interest—why didn't you think they would be suitable?'

'I got the distinct feeling they would have resented taking orders from a woman, Ross,' she said deliberately, and couldn't resist adding, 'I would have been quite capable of giving them short shrift myself, you know.'

She glanced at him and saw his lips twist. 'And with pleasure, no doubt,' he murmured. 'In lots of ways, you haven't changed at all.'

Ashley counted to ten carefully beneath her breath and managed to smile. 'You must be enjoying how . . . my chickens are coming home to roost, in a manner of speaking.'

He was silent and finally she took her eyes off the road briefly to look at him—which was a mistake, because his eyes were full of mockery again. When she looked away, he said softly, 'Doesn't it strike you as ironic that it was Laurie Lineham himself who placed you in this uncomfortable position?'

She clenched the wheel until her knuckles turned white, then with an effort forced herself to relax. 'We won't make Sydney until after dark—are you booked into a hotel?'

'Yes. The Hilton. Are you?'

Ashley bit her lip and he laughed quietly. 'Ditto?'

'Yes.'

'Never mind, you can always lock yourself in if you're afraid I might . . . attempt to take up where we once left off.'

She took her hand off the wheel and rubbed her forehead with her fingertips. 'If you keep on like this, I might . . . turn round and drive straight home,' she said huskily, and with an undercurrent of tension that she couldn't suppress. 'I don't *have* to put up with this. In fact,' she slowed the car and pulled off the road and brought it to a halt, 'I could just leave it all to you, seeing you're so determined to . . .' her voice shook, 'keep up this vendetta under the pretext of . . . of . . . oh, hell,' she said barely audibly, as she stared into his eyes and could see nothing but a curious alertness as he studied her in return.

'Giving up so soon, Ash?' he said, equally as quietly. 'I thought you had more spirit than that.'

Her shoulders sagged. 'It's not a question of . . .'

'Then what is it a question of?' he countered. 'You tell me. Is there something I'm not aware of that makes you look at me so proudly sometimes . . . as if you *never* gave me your body to be

possessed by a man for the first time, never took
your clothes off and showed me your beautiful
breasts . . .'

'Ross . . .' She said his name with a whimper of
pain.

But he ignored it and went on deliberately, 'As
if you never gasped with a mixture of fear and
hurt at first, then with delight, and you moved in
my arms to the tune of it, as if . . .'

Ashley turned away blindly and put the car into
gear, but he stopped her from driving off with a
hand on her arm and a curt, 'I'll drive for a while.
You'd be better relaxing.'

'Relaxing?' she whispered bitterly. 'You ask a
lot sometimes, Ross.' And she stared at him for a
moment, her eyes brimming with tears, then she
went back to neutral, put on the handbrake and
opened her door to slip out.

'Ashley,' he said abruptly, taking his hand
away but with his mouth still hard, 'did you
honestly expect you could walk back into my life
without one word of explanation, and find me all
sweetness and light and full of the spirit of
charity and forgiveness? No one could be that
naïve—or proud, surely?'

'I didn't *know* I was going to have to . . . Ross,'
she caught her breath at the almost murderous
glint in his eyes, and put her hands to her face,
distraught, then she took several deep breaths
and lifted her head. 'No. No, I knew I . . .
couldn't expect that, Ross.' Her lips trembled as
she glanced at him briefly, but a curious

composure—or perhaps it was a sense of defeat—came over her. 'No,' she said again very quietly, 'I always knew how it would be. If . . . if you wouldn't mind driving, it might be better.'

In fact, he drove all the way.

It was a curious drive. Once they'd changed places, the atmosphere seemed to change, and as Ashley stared out of the window at the landscape gliding by she reflected that she now felt like a prisoner in the charge of an efficient yet dispassionate guard. Ross had tuned the radio in to a one-day cricket game between Australia and New Zealand, and seemed content to accept her silence.

They stopped once when he bought them a belated lunch, then she fell asleep and didn't wake until they were on the outskirts of Sydney city and driving through a starlit night. He'd also retuned the radio and the car was, with the air-conditioner on and the windows closed, alive with Mozart, the soft, joyful tones of his 'Clarinet Concerto'.

Ashley lay with her head resting back, her eyes still half closed until the last note faded away—and Ross flicked the radio off. Then she turned her head to look at him as they drew up at a red light, and there must have been something unwittingly questioning and wary in her eyes because he said drily, 'It's all right—you don't have to look like that. Even an ogre like myself is not immune, apparently, to how defenceless you look asleep. We can resume hostilities in the morning.'

Ashley sat up and pulled the loosened jade green ribbon out of her hair. 'I don't usually fall asleep in cars,' she said huskily.

'Perhaps it was a *defensive* mechanism, then,' he suggested.

'Perhaps,' she murmured.

'Will you be able to sleep tonight?'

She glanced at him. 'Yes.'

'Lucky you. I have a client to meet, so after we've checked in I'll leave you to your own devices if you don't mind.'

'No. Isn't it . . . rather late to be meeting clients?'

He shrugged. 'To some people, nine-thirty—which is what it will be then—is early. But this is quite a serious matter.'

She started to say something about the time he must have wasted, driving down with her, but changed her mind and held her peace.

As if reading her mind, he remarked, 'My client wasn't available any earlier.'

'Oh.'

'How long are you planning to stay in Sydney?'

'Tomorrow and maybe Saturday. I thought I might do some shopping on Saturday morning and . . . drive home on Sunday. Are you . . .?' She stopped and bit her lip.

He drummed his fingers lightly on the steering-wheel at a dithering driver in front of him, and said gravely, 'I'm staying until Tuesday, you'll be relieved to hear. We're nearly there. How would it be if I meet you in the lobby tomorrow morning at nine-thirty? I believe your first interview is at ten.'

'Fine,' Ashley said steadily as he drove up the ramp and brought the Jaguar to a stop outside the portals of the Hilton. For a moment, as the commissionaire descended, they stared at each other, but she couldn't for the the life of her fathom the expression in his eyes, or explain why she got the feeling he was loath for their isolation from the outside world to end. Then she knew she'd been mistaken, as that glint of mockery she knew so well came into his eyes. She felt her cheeks redden as she wondered how *she* had looked, to put it there. Supplicatory? Something inside her shrank at the thought, and caused her to be brusque almost to the point of rudeness as they checked in, and as he walked her to the lift.

But all that achieved was his silent amusement, and as the lift doors closed on him her cheeks were red with embarrassment again.

CHAPTER FOUR

CONTRARY to her expectations, despite what she'd said to Ross, Ashley slept heavily and dreamlessly that night, although she woke early. And, after an hour of watching the sun rising, she had a shower and got dressed and decided to go for a walk before breakfast.

She got back to the hotel at about eight, and was hesitating in the lobby, wondering whether to have breakfast in the Market Garden restaurant or in her room, when Ross crossed her path.

'Ash,' he said with a grimace, 'you look all bright and brushed and beautiful.'

'You look as if you've been up all night,' she returned involuntarily, taking in the blue shadow on his jaw, the same clothes he'd had on yesterday and the lines of weariness beside his mouth.

'I have. My client is off to Singapore today—unexpectedly, so we had to make use of all the time left to us. Had breakfast?'

'No, I . . .'

'Good, then have it with me.' He turned towards the lifts.

'Ross, I . . .'

'My dear Ashley,' he turned back, 'I can assure

you I'm about as harmless as a butterfly at the moment, and I have only three aims in mind—to have a shower and get into some fresh clothes, to drink a gallon of orange juice to try to drown out the taste of all the coffee I've consumed, and to glance at the morning papers. So you'd be quite safe.'

Ashley raised an eyebrow. 'I don't see why you need my company, then.'

'I need it in case I fall asleep,' he replied promptly. 'Would it be such an imposition.'

'Ross, if . . .'

'I promise also to extend our truce,' he said lightly, then smothered a yawn. 'Please,' he added.

Ashley hesitated, then shrugged. 'All right.'

'It would help if you could try not to look as if you're going to the gallows,' he murmured.

Ashley took a breath and curbed her irritation as she wondered what was behind this new approach. But a brief, searching glance at him was unrevealing—beyond that the mockery she feared, and which she was becoming so used to seeing in his eyes, was not there.

'I . . . I'll try,' she said, conscious of the note of confusion in her voice.

'Good. So will I,' he said, barely audibly, and stood back for her to enter the lift.

His room had a different aspect, so she spent some time inspecting the view while he showered and she waited for the breakfast he'd ordered.

But, after a while, it was not the view of Sydney she found herself concentrating on, but her thoughts or, more accurately, her memories, those shadows on a screen, those precious memories she'd kept veiled in her heart and mind for so long . . .

It was a slight sound that brought her out of that reverie, and she turned with a suddenly pounding heart to find Ross standing right behind her, buttoning up his shirt, shaved and with his hair still damp and drops of water on his temples. For one dreadful moment the veil was ripped apart and there was no insulating distance between her and her memories of that long ago night, and him. Nothing to buffer what his nearness and the faint fresh tang of soap still clinging to his body recalled not only to mind but to her nerve-ends, so that her fingertips actually tingled as if she was touching his broad, smooth shoulders, smoothing them over the dark hair on his chest . . .

Her eyes dilated and he said with a sudden frown, 'What's wrong? Don't you feel well?'

'Fine! I feel fine, but . . . I'm starving,' she finished lamely, backing away at the same time as a knock came on the door.

'Saved by the bell,' he commented, but there was still a frown in his eyes as they rested on her.

'I missed dinner last night,' she murmured, and went to sit down.

'Talking of dinner—will you have dinner with me tomorrow night?' he said once the waiter had left.

Ashley smoothed her napkin in her lap. 'If . . . if I decide to stay,' she said uncertainly. 'I might go home tomorrow.'

He glinted her a suddenly sardonic look, but didn't pursue the subject. In fact, as they ate their breakfast, Ashley got the impression he was even trying to put her at her ease, but her mind was still reeling beneath the weight and impact of his closeness earlier, and she was thinking, I must have been mad to agree to . . . to *any* of this. He won't stay like this, he's still only toying with me, I know . . .

Yet throughout the morning Ross stayed exactly the same. He even took a back seat throughout the two interviews, and it was the second of these that finally struck gold.

Paddy Brown was a short, wiry man of forty who showed no inclination to be subtly patronising, he'd had considerable experience with sheep and there was a barely suppressed air of vitality and energy about him. He'd also brought his wife along, a homely, plump woman who'd been born and raised in the country and preferred it to the suburbs. They had two children, but both had left school and were working.

'You don't look old enough,' Ashley said with a grin.

'We started young,' Paddy Brown assured her, then cast his wife Mary a twinkling look, to which she responded with a wink.

That decided Ashley, and it was only as an afterthought that she turned to Ross with a raised eyebrow. He nodded, however, and she offered Paddy Brown the job on a mutual trial basis for three months there and then.

After the interview, she said to Ross, 'I can't tell you what a relief it is to have that settled.'

'Mmm.' He studied her for a moment and started to say something, then appeared to change his mind and change tack. 'While we're here, we might as well have a chat with the wool manager. I know him, and he's got his finger right on the pulse. You do have the option of buying a ram to introduce new blood to the flock, but I've got a feeling we might have missed the boat.'

Frank Evans was a bluff, friendly man with those very blue eyes one associates with a farmer continually scanning the horizon, but he also had a lot of up-to-date figures at his fingertips, and after discussing the wool indicator for a while he moved on to Ashley's options for upgrading her flock—buying a ram or using a programme of artificial insemination from carefully chosen, commercially marketed semen.

'In the long term, Mrs Lineham, a ram is a good business proposition, as you probably know,' he said to Ashley, 'because then *you're* in the position to market its semen; but I must tell you that the record price just jumped a few months ago from forty-seven thousand to a hundred and ten thousand for a Poll Merino ram in South Australia.'

Ashley looked wryly at Ross. 'I think we'll have to think about that.'

And finally they were out in noon sunlight, strolling along the crowded pavements towards the hotel.

Ross said, 'A productive morning. I'm only sorry I can't offer you lunch to celebrate, but have you thought any more about having dinner with me tomorrow night?'

Ashley stopped walking for a moment and looked up at him. 'I . . . all right,' she said a little breathlessly. 'Thank you for your help.'

'A pleasure, ma'am,' he said gravely, then glanced at his watch.

'Don't worry about me now if you have an appointment . . .'

'I do. Unfortunately I have wall-to-wall appointments this afternoon and tomorrow, but say . . . six-thirty tomorrow evening? I'll meet you in the lobby.'

'Yes. Goodbye . . .'

'So long,' he said with a grin as he walked away, but Ashley remained where she was, staring after him, unconscious of the obstruction she was causing until someone tapped her on the shoulder. 'Ashley—it *is* you! My dear, how lovely to see you!'

'Oh!' She started and swung round to find herself confronted by a middle-aged couple who had been among Laurence Lineham's best friends and were moreover two people who had gone out of their way to welcome her into their circle. Within ten minutes she found herself seated in a nearby restaurant with them for lunch, and by the time lunch ended she had accepted their invitation to go to the races at Rose Hill with them the following afternoon.

Back in her hotel room much later, she found herself feeling a little dazed and regretting the races tomorrow.

Why? she mused, as she changed into something loose and comfortable. They're darlings and they were good friends. I think . . . it's Ross. I'm . . . I feel as if I'm skating on such thin ice with him, it's affecting everything I do. Why did he change like that? I can only . . . no, I can't ever hope.

She sat down and pleated her dress between her fingers, then with a desolate little sigh laid her head back and closed her eyes.

The next morning she decided to avail herself of the hotel's beauty parlour, where she had the works: a facial, a manicure and her hair washed and blow-dried. Then she went shopping for a suitable outfit for the races—as a guest of members of the Sydney turf club who also had two runners on a feature race day, she knew she should dress up and had brought nothing suitable.

Her purchases were expensive but timelessly elegant, and when she finally studied herself in a turquoise silk suit, a matching finest straw broad-brimmed hat and black accessories, she couldn't help feeling pleased, although a little rueful. The outfit had been an extravagant gesture, but then she consoled herself with the thought that she hadn't bought any new clothes for a long time and—the suit would be equally suitable for dinner.

She stared at her reflection in the mirror and saw her lips tremble and the way her grey eyes looked. And she whispered to herself, 'No, don't get your hopes up, don't do that to yourself, not yet . . .'

Half-way through the afternoon, she realised her regret at accepting this invitation had not been solely to do with Ross. Her hosts weren't deficient in any way, they were marvellous, but as she stood in the saddling paddock, watching the riders mount for the feature race, and surrounded by all the noise and colour of what had been one of Laurie's favourite milieux, she was assailed by a sense of sadness and strain.

After the races they were caught in a traffic jam on the way back to the hotel, and she realised she was going to be late for Ross. Also the strain had transmitted itself to the beginnings of a headache.

She was twenty minutes late in the end, but she'd explained the situation to her hosts and had made her farewells so that, as they drew up outside the Hilton, she was able to leave the car with a final goodbye and thank you, and a wave. She turned to go inside immediately, and all but bumped into Ross.

'Oh! Oh, I'm so sorry I'm late—we got caught up in some traffic. Did you think I'd . . .' She stopped abruptly, realising she was gabbling, and that he was standing with his hands shoved into his pockets and with an inscrutable expression in his dark eyes, as he took in her elegant suit, the beautiful hat, her flushed, breathless appearance.

'Did I think you'd run off again?' he drawled, at last. 'I must admit I was beginning to wonder. Old friends?' he queried.

'Well, old friends of Laurie's really,' she said without thinking, and flinched at the darkness that came over his face. 'I . . . bumped into them yesterday after you . . . left me, and they invited me to the races.'

'Did they, now?' His lips twisted.

'Ross——' she said uncertainly.

He raised an eyebrow and waited.

'Oh, nothing,' she murmured, half turning away. 'Where are we eating?'

'Here, if you approve.'

'Yes,' she whispered, 'of course.'

But it was a dimly lit, comfortable and cool bar he led her into with an abrupt, 'We'll have a drink first.'

Ashley sank down thankfully and took off her hat.

'That's a relief,' she said, with an attempt at a smile and rubbing her brow. 'It—or something—was giving me a headache.'

'Sure you're up to having dinner?'

Ashley looked at him, at the glitter in his eyes, and her fingers on her forehead faltered. Her hand sank into her lap, then rose again in a hopeless little gesture as she said, 'I knew it was too good to be true . . .'

'Knew what was too good to be true?' he asked roughly.

'How you were—you're angry again and . . . and . . .' She couldn't go on.

'That's very acute of you, Ashley,' he marvelled.

'Why? I mean . . .' She swallowed.

'You can't even think why?' he taunted.

Ashley put her hand to her mouth, then stood up clumsily. 'I meant—why change, why bother . . . oh!' And she turned away blindly, knocking into a chair.

He was up on his feet in a flash, steadying her with a hard hand on her elbow. 'Where do you think you're going?' he said through his teeth.

'Upstairs . . . anywhere. I knew this could never work.'

'Then perhaps it's time we found out why.' He reached for her hat and handed it to her.

'Ross . . .'

'We'll go upstairs together. Don't argue, Ashley,' he said curtly as he steered her out of the bar and across the lobby to the lifts. 'We'll try your room this time,' he added with a sardonic smile, and pressed the button for floor forty-three.

'I . . .' His dark gaze captured hers, and what she saw in it caused a little pulse of panic to beat at the base of her throat. 'Ross . . .'

But the lift stopped at the forty-third floor, and he took her suddenly nerveless free hand and led her out. 'Got your key?' He released her hand.

'I . . .' She delved into her bag. 'Yes, but . . .'

He took it, looked at the number briefly and turned unerringly in the right direction.

And outside her door she stood stock still as he opened it, her face pale, her eyes dark and riveted to his. She knew from the suddenly hard, determined set of his mouth that he would have no compunction about forcing her to go in with him.

She lowered her lashes but tilted her chin and walked through the doorway as composedly as she was able. He followed, closing the door behind him.

She stood in the middle of the room with her back to him for a moment, then turned and started to speak.

'I suppose . . .'

'I wouldn't, if I were you, make too many suppositions, Ashley,' he murmured, looming over her and taking her hat, bag and gloves from her to toss them on to the bed. He switched on a lamp and came back to her.

'Ross,' she whispered.

'Until we test out what was once fact. You know—and I'm sorry to keep harping on the subject,' he said barely audibly, the lines of

his face harsh as he studied her from beneath
half-closed lids—her mouth, no longer bravely
painted as it had been earlier, the column of her
neck where it disappeared into the collar of her
jacket, 'but you came to me rather like this, one
night, with no explanations just . . . naked
desire.' He raised a hand and caressed her throat.
'You also left with no explanations, like a thief in
the night . . . It's my turn now. There's an old
saying about an eye for an eye, isn't there?'

She made a small, inarticulate sound as he slid
his hand round and spread his fingers through
her hair at the nape of her neck, tugging gently.
' "Kiss me, Ross," ' he murmured, scanning her
upturned face. 'Does that ring a bell? Oh, I
believe you said please—anyway, I obliged. I
think it's up to you to return the compliment.'
And he lowered his head to kiss her.

Ashley went rigid, then tried to pull away, but
his arms were suddenly around her and they were
like steel bands, impossible to fight, crushing her.
She moaned, but that was a mistake because,
although he lessened the pressure, he took full
advantage of her parted lips.

It was a savage kiss he subjected her to, a
punishment, she thought dimly, that left her
dizzy and clinging to him helplessly, her lips
swollen, her eyes frightened. It also left him
breathing heavily as he raised his head at last, and
there was a hard, mocking glint in his
eyes—mockery, she thought, because he had her
so much at his mercy until he spoke, and she

realised the mockery was also self-directed.

'You had more finesse, didn't you, Ashley?' he said very softly, raising a hand to touch her lips. 'Sorry. Let's see if I can made amends.'

And before she had time to think he slid his hand down to the buttons of her jacket, flicking them open to her waist.

'Ross . . . Ross, no,' she whispered despairingly.

He took no notice, just moved her away a little and completed the task. Her jacket fell open, revealing that all she had on beneath was a black, lacy bra. He slid the turquoise silk of the suit off one shoulder slowly, and the lamplight gilded her smooth, satiny skin and her breasts gleamed pearly white beneath the black lace.

She swallowed, licked her lips and made a movement, but he stilled it with a brief, warning glance and then released her, but only, with utter absorption, to remove the jacket entirely. It fell down her arms and to the floor behind her with the soft slither of silk. He held her at arm's length, his hand cupping her shoulders.

Ashley closed her eyes and stood with her head bent, her hair falling forward like a dark curtain, and, as if his hands were upon them, felt her nipples harden into peaks so sensitive that the black lace felt scratchy and unbearable. And that sensation travelled down her body to the core of her sensuality, so that she shuddered slightly, and knew she was possessed of desire—that the long years of fighting this feeling for Ross and Ross alone had been wasted because it still only needed his eyes and hands upon her to kindle it . . .

She looked up through her lashes, and with a small sound of despair released the front opening of her bra.

Her breasts were fuller now, lower, her nipples darker, and he gazed at them, touched each throbbing peak lightly so that she trembled, then gathered her into his arms. 'Did you feed Susie?'

She nodded into his shoulder and felt a current of tension run through him, and when he held her away again the darkness was back in his expression, the set of his mouth was hard. Then he released her abruptly, bent down for her jacket and handed it to her and turned away.

'Ross . . .' She crumpled the turquoise silk to her defensively, hiding her naked breasts fearfully now. 'Ross, there's something . . .'

He swung back and raised a sardonic eyebrow at her.

'Something?'

'I . . . I should explain.' She stopped and looked away.

'Go on,' he said harshly. 'Or perhaps I can guess? Is it to do with this embarrassing business of finding yourself still wanting me?'

'Would you believe that I . . . never stopped?' she asked huskily.

'Even although you went ahead and bore another man's child?' he queried.

Their gazes locked until Ashley's fell away first and she thought agonisedly, if I explain . . . how can I ever explain it all?

'Ashley?'

'Nothing . . . I mean, it doesn't matter, Ross. Please go away. That's what you were going to do anyway, wasn't it?' she said jerkily. She looked down at herself and felt something inside her shrivel, and in its place an odd sense of defiance came over her. She raised her head proudly. 'I hope this victory is . . . sweet,' she said bitterly.

He stared at her, then murmured, 'I'll reserve judgement on that. I'll probably be cursing myself for a fool shortly. Offers as . . . blatant as yours don't come my way every day. You know,' he lifted a hand and touched her hair fleetingly, and she flinched away, 'your hair is beautiful. Don't ever cut it. It was one of the first things I . . . noticed about you, and what a difference it made when you took it out of its pigtail.'

'Get out,' she whispered.

A faint smile touched his lips. 'That was the other thing I noticed straight away. Your Crawford arrogance.' He turned on his heel and left.

Ashley stayed where she was for a long time after the door closed, then she lay down on the bed, still hugging her jacket to her uncaringly, and wept.

As fate would have it, when she left the next morning and took the lift down to reception, it stopped twice on the way down. Once to admit two talkative, elderly American tourists, once to admit Ross.

It was no consolation to Ashley that he looked tired and strained, because nothing hid the way his dark eyes roamed over her, leaving her in no doubt that he was seeing her half-naked. And she found herself praying that her famed arrogance would not desert her now and reveal the awful feeling of vulnerability their encounter the previous evening had left her with.

Help was at hand from an unexpected source, she discovered as they stepped into the foyer. A blonde girl in her early twenties ran up to him excitedly, saying, 'Ross, darling! I only got your message this morning because I only got back from Perth last night after the most trying flight! Dozens of babies all sicking up because of turbulence—I just crashed into bed, but I've got two free days . . .'

Ashley met his eyes over the blonde girl's head, then she turned away and went to pay her bill. But, as she drove the Jaguar up the New England highway, she was conscious of a hardening within her like an iron sense of determination, so strong that her neck and jaw ached until she forced herself to relax.

The next morning, Monday, she went into town and got her hair cut.

'Ashley! Oh, I like it,' Tasha said enthusiastically. 'Can I get mine cut the same way? It has a marvellous sort of boyish chic, especially the way it falls over your forehead, and it looks stunning with those gorgeous tiny pearls in your ears!'

Ashley smiled ruefully. 'If you like, Tasha, but your hair's so curly, I'm not sure it would look the same.'

Tasha sighed heavily—her red curls and freckles were the bane of her life.

Maggie, however, was scandalised. 'What on earth have you done to yourself, Ashley Crawford?' she demanded. 'Have you gone mad?'

'I'm no longer Ashley Crawford,' Ashley murmured. 'And no, I'm quite sane.'

'But it was . . . your crowning glory! Now you look like a . . . a glorified boy!'

'Which is exactly what I plan to be—not glorified, but as hard-working as. This hairstyle is practical, especially in summer. End of subject,' she added firmly.

But Maggie had the last word. 'You always could be a bit hoity-toity,' she remarked, and took herself out to her vegetable garden to search for any ravages Bob Mulhall's dogs might have wreaked.

It was Susie, not Tasha, who ended up with a similar haircut, much to Maggie's disapproval when Ashley brought her home from the hairdresser. 'Well, what was I supposed to do?' Ashley enquired. 'Leave it as it was?'

Maggie could only snort, because Susie had begun the process herself with a pair of nail scissors. Then her eyes narrowed as they rested on Susie's face. 'Gives her the look of . . .'

She stopped short.

'I look like Mummy now,' Susie said proudly.

For the next three weeks, Ashley worked harder than she ever had. So hard that she lost weight and was only too happy to tumble into bed at night after quiet evenings spent with the girls. In a week, Tasha would be returning to boarding-school and was already grumbling about it—and particularly at having to be parted from Cornflower. But Ashley was happy to see how well Tasha had adapted to such a different life-style. Poor kid, she sometimes thought, but not nearly as often as when Tasha had first come to live with her father after her mother's death, an aggressive but inwardly bereft twelve-year-old, coping with not only grief but a strange stepmother and a new half-sister.

It occurred to Ashley, and it was oddly comforting, she found, to think that while she might have made an awful mess of her life in other respects she'd done a good job with Tasha. Here's hoping I can do the same with Susie—I will, she vowed. After all, that's my main aim in life now.

Paddy Brown and his wife moved into the renovated manager's cottage, and it was soon clear Ashley had not underestimated his energy or capability. What was more, she felt that with the Browns and Bob Mulhall she'd established a small community which would benefit Susie particularly. There were a few anxious moments

—Maggie didn't take to newcomers readily, but Mary Brown was so quietly and unassumingly capable, she soon won the old lady's approval.

Of Ross, Ashley managed to blank her mind by a supreme effort of will. Until he sought her out.

It had been a blindingly hot day and the heat was still lingering, although the sun was starting to set when Ashley drove the van into the shed, climbed out wearily and started to unload some gear from the back.

Her overalls were dirty, the blue check shirt she wore beneath them was sticking to her back and she was dying to get out of the short riding-boots she wore. It was as she picked up the shotgun she'd taken with her, because there was evidence of dingoes on the property, that an unexpected sound stopped her in her tracks and she swung round with the gun in her hand.

It was Ross, lounging beside the shed door, watching her.

He straightened and drawled, his gaze flickering from the gun to her face. 'Dear me—that's a bit extreme, isn't it?'

Ashley compressed her lips, then spoke without stopping to think. 'It did the trick once . . .' She broke off and turned away to put the gun up on a high rack in a cupboard.

'And what's that supposed to mean?' he asked from behind her.

Ashley locked the cupboard and pocketed the keys. 'Nothing,' she said curtly, and turned to face him resolutely. 'What are you doing here?'

'I brought some documents for you to sign, as a matter of fact,' he said casually, but his dark gaze lingered on her hair. 'That's quite a . . . statement, isn't it?'

'What do you mean?'

'Did you go out and get it cut off just to . . .?'

'Ross,' she interrupted coolly, 'it's none of your business.' She stared at him, then said, 'But yes, I guess you're right. It is a statement. I'm tired of men . . . I'm tired of being this or that to men, I'm tired of being manipulated by them for their *own* purposes. I have no desire any more to even be attractive to them . . .'

'If you think cutting your hair is going to change that,' he said with a mocking little smile, 'you're mistaken. It actually suits you,' he added, folding his arms as he studied her meditatively. 'My mistake,' he said softly.

Ashley ground her teeth. 'Get out of my way,' she ordered, realising he was barring her path to the door. 'I'm hot and tired . . .'

'And spitting mad . . . All right, I will—when you tell me how a gun did the trick for you once. Did you find yourself having to protect your virtue with one?'

'Yes, I did.'

'How dramatic,' he murmured. 'Did you see it in a movie?'

Ashley's eyes glinted. 'I read it in a book, as it happens, and I thought—if it can work for her, it can work for me. Satisfied?'

He laughed. 'That's my Ashley! You never lacked spirit. Who was it who found himself on the receiving end of a gun, with you no doubt breathing fire and brimstone at him?'

'Ross,' Ashley said through her teeth and fishing the keys out of her pocket again, 'don't tempt me . . .'

Their gazes locked, and for a moment she saw a quizzical gleam in his eyes that told her her bravado was wasted on him; then, as a tide of furious exasperation rose in her, he sobered and said abruptly, 'You've lost weight. What are you doing to yourself? Working yourself to the bone just to prove an unprovable point?'

'We'll see about that,' she said tightly. 'Let me pass.'

He did.

She stalked out of the shed, then her shoulders slumped because Susie and Tasha were approaching eagerly, obivously filled with delight to see Ross.

'Have a shower, I'll spend some time with them,' he said quietly from right behind her. 'Maggie's invited me to stay for dinner, and I thought I'd have a chat with Bob, catch up on old times.'

Ashley thought of saying—feel free, why don't you just move in? But she suddenly found herself right out of energy.

She stayed in the shower for a long time, meditating beneath the soothing needles of water on the fact that Ross was so curiously implacable in one way or another. If not by direct confrontation, in this way. Beguiling Susie and Tasha, making himself almost a part of the family.

'What does he want from me?' she murmured to herself. 'Will he only be satisfied if I get down on my knees and confess that it was a terrible mistake to marry Laurie? But even then, would the truth satisfy him . . . or fill him with rage and disgust, more than ever? How much did the *least* important aspect of it all affect him? The fact that I was a Crawford and he was an illegitimate foster child . . .

She stepped out of the shower at last, and it crossed her mind to wonder how he could tell, beneath baggy overalls, that she'd lost weight?

'I'm not precisely down to scarecrow proportions,' she mused, staring at her steamy reflection in the bathroom mirror. 'Does he know me so . . . well?'

She turned away.

She dressed in jeans and a pink shirt, and slid her feet into flat sandals with a sigh of relief, reflecting wryly that all she had to do was run her hands through her damp hair for it to fall into place.

Bob, Ross and Maggie were having a sundowner on the front veranda when she emerged, with Tasha playing hostess.

'Sit down, Ash,' she invited. 'Something long and cool?'

'Thanks, Tasha. Well, this is very pleasant,'

she murmured.

Bob cocked an eyebrow at her. He was a tall, leathery man with a fierce white moustache and a dry sense of humour. 'Any signs of dingoes?'

'Not even a track this morning.' She accepted a frosted glass from Tasha and sipped gratefully.

'Been having trouble?' Ross enquired.

'Think it's only a loner,' Bob pronounced. 'Probably a wily old dog, and I suspect, if he takes any more, we'll only get him with an organised hunt.'

'Well, let me know if you do decide to organise a hunt, I'll lend a hand,' Ross offered.

'Oh, a shooting party, and I bet I'll be back at school!' Tasha lamented.

'You wouldn't be allowed on it, even if you weren't,' Maggie said tartly. 'Young ladies don't need to know about that kind of thing.'

'I bet Ashley did,' Tasha replied pertly.

'Ashley was a law unto herself occasionally,' Maggie said repressively. 'I know there were times she regretted it.'

Ashley looked up to find Ross watching her particularly. 'So I did—so I did, Tasha,' she managed to say wryly. 'Where's Susie?'

'I'm here,' a voice piped up from the lawn below the veranda. 'I'm teaching Georgie tricks. Ross said he had a dog once that could shake hands, but I don't think Georgie knows his paws can be hands.'

Ross put his drink down and stood up. 'I'll come down and give you a hand—or a paw,' he

said with a grin, and Tasha giggled as he strolled
down the steps. Moments later he and Susie
could be heard seriously discussing how to train
dogs.

Ashley stared at the horizon as the last
lingering pink of the sunset left the sky. Then she
said brightly, 'I'm starving.'

After dinner, Ross brought out the documents
and they sat at the cleared dining-room table
discussing them. There were certain short-term
investments in the girls' inheritances up for
renewal and or re-investment. Ross described
what he thought would be the best course for
them, and Ashley listened carefully, saying
finally, 'Yes, that sounds sensible. Thank you.'

He pushed the papers into his briefcase and
looked around for his jacket and tie, then looked
back at her and said abruptly, 'Are you as
exhausted as you look?'

Ashley blinked. 'No.'

'Have the girls gone to bed?'

'Yes. Why?'

He got up and closed the dining-room door and
wandered around the room, then leant back
against the dresser and stared at her. 'The last
time we . . . were together, you said there was
something you should explain. I . . . wasn't
precisely in the mood for explanations.' He
shrugged slightly and his eyes were sombre. 'If
that was unfair to you, I apologise. Will you tell
me now what you wanted to tell me then?'

Ashley's gaze fell away, she licked her lips and the minutes ticked by. Then she said with an effort, 'I wanted to explain that my marriage to Laurie was . . . a marriage of convenience, and that I was . . . forced into it.'

Ross stared at her, then he said drily, 'Marriages of convenience are slightly outdated, aren't they?' He stopped and narrowed his eyes. 'On the other hand,' he said meditatively, 'perhaps your father was enough of a bastard to make you think you had to do something like that. Is *that* . . . what you're trying to tell me?' he said softly and incredulously. 'But—why?'

'He . . . he was going bankrupt,' Ashley said with an effort.

'There was no sign of it.'

'He managed to keep it quiet somehow. Until . . . until Laurie found out and used it.'

'So we have two villains?' His gaze was sardonic.

Ashley closed her eyes. 'It's true,' she whispered. 'You said yourself you were surprised Laurie left me so little. In effect, he left me Crawford Downs because, without him, it wouldn't have been mine to inherit after my father died.

'And you . . . *knew* all this when you came to me that night?' The disbelief in his voice made Ashley flinch.

She took a breath. 'Yes. I thought I had no choice. I thought it was the one way I could repay my father for his disappointment . . .'

'That you weren't a boy,' Ross supplied roughly. 'That was hardly your fault.'

'All the same . . .'

'And where, as a matter of interest, did I fit in?'

'Ross,' she said huskily, 'you *always* held me at arm's length.'

'Would you rather I'd seduced you when you were seventeen?' he asked grimly. 'I know you might have then, but now, looking back?'

A slow tide of colour rose up Ashley's throat. 'But still, when I was nineteen . . .' She gestured helplessly.

'When you were nineteen, Ashley,' he countered, 'if I'd asked you to marry me or so much as laid a finger on you, there'd still have been hell to pay. I had nothing going for me—other than hopes, nothing but the breadline to offer you. And there was no way I was to know whether a complete break with your father and Crawford Downs—and it could have happened even without what I didn't know—was in your best interest. You may not believe this, but all those years I spent holding you at arm's length were for your own good. But that's an entirely different thing to standing by and watching you being forced to marry Laurie Lineham——' He stopped abruptly.

'Did I mean something to you then, Ross?' she whispered, her grey eyes tormented.

He stared at her. 'You meant the world to me, Ashley,' he said grimly and quietly. 'I watched you grow up virtually, I watched you . . . dying

to please your father, going through the torture of
trying to be a son for him while you were
flowering into womanhood, I watched you fight
the effect we had on each other, and it was a good
fight—then you laid down your arms and I
thought you'd understood it was time to grow
together quietly, that it would be fatal to rush it,
to flaw it. I watched you . . . oh, what the hell!'
He moved away from the dresser and sat down
and stared across the room until presently he
said, 'So you didn't love him?'

'Laurie? No. Not that way. I . . . we became
friends, though.'

Ross turned his dark gaze to her, and his eyes
were insolently incredulous. 'I find it hard to
believe you could become friends with a man who
connived with your father to force you to marry
him.'

'He was . . .' Ashley sought for the right words.

'Did he force you to sleep with him? I take it,
on the evidence, that it wasn't Lineham you used
a gun against to protect your virtue.'

'He . . . he wasn't capable of sleeping with me
for a long time before he died,' she whispered.

Ross raised an eyebrow. 'How unfortunate for
him,' he murmured. 'Is that why you were so
receptive to me in Sydney?'

Ashley moved and bit her lip.

'Ashley?' he drawled.

Ashley willed herself to stay calm. 'I know it's
not easy to understand. Looking back now, I . . .
I can't believe I did it.'

'Did what?' he said softly but menacingly. 'Slept with me or married him?'

Ashley veiled her eyes. 'Slept with you, Ross, the way I did it. Because I always knew you'd never be able to forgive me. But at least you know the truth now . . .' She lifted her lashes and stared at him, her face pale but composed, yet curiously still and expectant.

'You were right,' he said. Something died in her eyes, and he frowned suddenly. 'Ash——'

'Ross,' she cut in, 'I think we've said it all now. Can we end the war?' she said intensely, and as if her nerves were strained to breaking-point. 'If it's any consolation, I'll never forgive *myself*.' She slumped back, exhausted.

'There is,' he said slowly, 'still the question of what we mean to each other now.'

'I *know* what I mean to you now,' she said tiredly. 'You've never stopped making that perfectly plain since I came back.'

'I was labouring under certain disillusions . . .'

'You've just told me it makes no difference, you still can't forgive me—well, I can do no more. It's one of those things, those misguided things that happen to you when you're . . . young and foolish. I admit all that, but at the time I didn't know which way to turn . . .'

'Not even . . . after we'd made love and you were lying in my arms . . .?'

'Stop it, Ross.'

'Was it—the way you gave yourself to me that

night—was it an act of defiance, Ashley?
Were you saying to your father and Laurence
Lineham . . .'

'Ross . . . all right,' she said with tears suddenly
streaming down her face, 'it was an act of *despair*.
Do you remember what you were doing that
night . . . the night I came? You told me you'd
just scraped your last cent together to buy out old
Mr Bell's practice in town. You told me it was
going to be even more of a gamble than you
thought because you'd just learnt that another
solicitor was opening up in opposition, but that at
least you had some established clients—if you
could keep them. Do you *know* what some well-
chosen words from my father to some of those
established clients who were bound to be friends
would have achieved?'

He was silent, his mouth set in a hard line, his
eyes glittering oddly.

'Do you know,' she went on barely audibly,
wiping her face convulsively, 'that it was no idle
threat of his to run you out of town when I told
him how I felt about you, and that the only
reason he *didn't* was because it was part of the
bargain I made with him.'

'You believed him?' His voice was harsh and
she shrank back a little as he sat up. There was
anger in every line of his body.

'Yes,' she whispered, however, 'I believed
him.'

'In fact, you believed everybody but me,
Ashley.'

'Ross . . .'

'So I owe everything I've achieved to your . . . sacrifice and your father's magnanimous gesture?'

'No, but . . .'

'Well, I think that's what you're trying to tell me, Ashley, and I suppose it would be churlish not to be grateful.' He looked at her mockingly. 'But none of this would have happened if you'd trusted me to take care of both of our futures. Neither your father nor Laurie Lineham would have stopped me. You see, I've spent nearly all my life fighting for what I want, so it's nothing new to me.' He stood up. 'Don't cry, my dear. We all have our points of pride, I guess. It's just a pity you had the misfortune to expose mine.' And he left the room.

Ashley closed her eyes, but they flew open as she heard short, sharp words being exchanged outside the door, then Maggie came in, her face red but her expression murderous.

'There, there,' she said, sitting down and taking Ashley's hand.

'You were listening!'

'Heard every word,' Maggie said grimly, and not without some pride, 'and you listen to me, that's the last time you go down on your knees for any man. They don't deserve it, none of 'em.'

'I should never have come back because I knew . . . you heard,' Ashley wept. 'What if he ever . . .'

'There's nothing he can do, Ashley. Just remember that, love. And you did what you thought you had to. If he can't understand, that's his problem, but I tell you what, he won't find he's so welcome here any more!'

'Where's Ross?' Susie said out of the blue, several weeks later.

'Licking his wounded pride, no doubt,' Maggie muttered.

'Why does everybody go away and stay 'way?' Susie went on.

Ashley and Maggie exchanged glances over her head.

'I've been wanting to show him how Georgie shakes hands now. He *said* he would come and see it.'

'I—guess he's very busy, darling,' Ashley said. 'But Tasha will be home for the long weekend in a few weeks, so you can show her.'

Susie brightened, but later Ashley heard her telling the dog she was sure Ross had not forgotten and that he'd come one day.

And over the next few days Susie's keenness to see Ross again stayed on Ashley's mind, until the tension she felt was almost unbearable. When an opportunity for a break came up, she decided to take it.

'Maggie—oh, there you are. Mag, I'm going away for a couple of days.' She leant against the kitchen-table and put her foot on a chair so she could rub her ankle. 'Tomorrow.' She named a famous sheep station to the west of Crawford Downs. 'They're having an open day, a seminar the next day on breeding, etcetera, and I think I could learn a lot. Would you mind if I left Susie with you? It'll be as hot as hell and boring for her, and . . .'

'If you think I'd let you take the little one to one of those fly-blown bashes, you're mistaken,' Maggie said crossly, and with unspoken implication that Ashley was mad to want to go herself. 'Where will you stay overnight?'

Ashley grinned. 'I'll drive into the nearest town and sleep at a motel, Maggie.'

Maggie grunted, then cast Ashley a critical look. 'What *is* wrong with that ankle? I've noticed you limping the last couple of days.'

Ashly grimaced. 'To be honest, I don't know. I think I must have tripped and wrenched it without realising it.'

'Then you'd best be off it! Not . . .'

'Maggie . . .'

'Or if not that,' Maggie said determinedly, 'taking it to the doctor.'

'There's no need for that.' Ashley returned Maggie's unwavering blue stare and sighed. 'Oh, all right. I'll stop in and see him on my way tomorrow or on the way back——'

'Tomorrow,' Maggie said, rinsing her hands and reaching for the phone. 'What time? I'll give them a ring and make the appointment.'

'Don't you trust me, Maggie?'

'No. What time?'

'Nine o'clock.'

*   *   *

That night she explained to Susie about the trip,
and searched her little face anxiously for any sign
of apprehension at being left behind or that she
had secret fears of Ashley joining the group of
people who seemed to walk out of her young life.
But it seemed that Susie trusted her not to do
this, and she went to sleep peacefully after her
bedtime story.

Ashley stared down at her for a long time, then
went to bed early herself.

As she drove into town the next morning, with
Maggie's admonition not to forget her doctor's
appointment ringing in her ears and with a small
bag of clothes in the boot, she acknowledged to
herself that although her ankle was more painful,
if anything, the real reason she resented being
bulldozed into visiting the doctor was because his
surgery happened to be next door to Ross's office.

How ridiculous, she mused.

Ridiculous or not, it was with a sigh of relief
that she got into the waiting-room without
encountering Ross. In fact, his office appeared to
be closed.

The doctor agreed with her diagnosis of what
must have happened to her ankle, and suggested
some ultrasound treatment and in the event of
her being unable to stay off it, a walking-stick.

'I've even got one I could lend you. Someone
left it here months ago and has never come back
to collect it.'

Ashley looked doubtful as he retrieved a plain
cane stick from a cupboard and gave her a few

instructions for its use.

'I feel about ninety,' she said with a grin, 'but you're right, it does help.'

'It will also help to have a support bandage on it—I'll put one on for you after we've done the ultrasound.'

'Now I feel like a ninety-year-old horse,' Ashley commented after the treatment.

'If I may say so, Mrs Lineham,' the doctor, who was young and careful and kind, said with an appreciative look, 'you're much more like a best-bred champion filly . . .' He stopped and looked rueful. 'I meant that as a compliment.'

Ashley laughed. 'Thank you. I happen to like horses too, so I'll accept it as a compliment.'

And indeed, it seemed to buck her up, because she left his surgery feeling almost jaunty, only to come to grief almost immediately.

She was never sure whether it was the walking-stick or a crack in the pavement, or simply the sight of Pamela Flint inserting her key into the door next door, that caused her to stumble and her weak ankle to twist so that she ended up on her knees.

'Oh!' Pamela turned round. 'Why, Ashley—are you all right? Here, let me help you up.'

'Thank you—I'm fine really, Mrs Flint,' Ashley said breathlessly then, 'Damn!' as she brushed her jeans.

Pamela followed her gaze to a dirty streak on the left kneecap of her jeans. 'Look,' she said immediately, 'come in. I can try to wash that out for you, and you can tell me why you're hobbling about on a walking-stick!'

'That's very kind of you, Mrs Flint, but . . .'

'Ross is away on holiday,' Pamela said casually, but with a penetrating look at Ashley's red cheeks. 'You've got one very dirty hand, too,' she added.

Ashley looked at her hand and grimaced. 'I tried to save myself . . .' She hesitated, but Pamela was looking determined now and she had the door open. Ashley could only say lamely, 'Thank you, it's very kind of you.'

Ten minutes later, the dirty streak had been reduced to a damp patch, Ashley had washed her hands and was sitting in the outer office sipping some lovely hot, strong coffee. 'How long has Ross gone away for?' she asked, trying to sound only idly enquiring.

'He said a week. It's the first holiday he's taken for ages and he really needs it,' Pamela said expressively, and with a rueful little smile. 'I told him he's been like a bear with a sore head lately and . . . what is it?' She put her cup down as Ashley, who was staring out of the window, went pale, and she turned and an expression of exasperation crossed her face as she saw that a familiar blue car had pulled into the kerb. 'Well, really,' she said indignantly, 'either he's forgotten to tell me something, or he believes I can't cope on my own and . . .' She stopped abruptly as Ashley stood up tensely, the little bell on the door tinkled, and Ross strode in.

For a moment no one spoke, then Ross drawled,

'Good morning, Mrs Lineham. This is a surprise.'

'Ross,' Pamela said chidingly, 'you're not supposed to be here!'

'So I gather.' He turned his dark, mocking gaze on her.

Pamela looked briefly surprised, then annoyed, and in very precise, almost legal jargon, she explained what had happened and went on to further explain why Ashley had a weak ankle in the first place. And, as she finished, her expression said quite clearly—put that in your pipe and smoke it, Ross Reid!

This was obviously not lost on Ross, because with a cool smile he said sardonically, 'My dear Pamela, your Good Samaritan tendencies are quite laudable. Nor is Ashley barred from the premises—she is, after all, a client. Please—feel free to invite her for coffee any time you like. Do you have the mail?'

Ashley opened her mouth to intervene, but Pamela Flint was quite capable of dealing with Ross, she discovered. 'I do,' that good lady said arctically, drawing herself up to her full five foot two. 'But if you care to recall, you're supposed to be on holiday. If you've changed your mind, would you be so good as to inform me whether you're here for a day, a week or whatever? I am not a clairvoyant!'

Ashley held her breath, but after a moment Ross said gravely, 'My apologies, Mrs Flint. I *think* I need a cup of your excellent coffee with which to . . . start the day again.'

Pamela compressed her lips, then she chuckled. 'One coffee coming up!' And she disappeared into the kitchenette.

Ross transferred his gaze to Ashley with an eyebrow slightly raised.

'I'll get going,' she said awkwardly. 'I'm going away for a couple of days myself, so . . .'

'I didn't see your car,' he cut in.

'It's around the corner.' Ashley bit her lip and fell silent, cursing herself for sounding guilty.

'Where are you going?'

She explained briefly.

'Tramping around some open day is not going to help your ankle,' he said impatiently. 'Bring your coffee into my office.'

'Ross . . .'

He shot her an irritable look. 'I'm not really in a mood to be argued with, Ashley—oh, thanks, Pam,' he murmured as he accepted a steaming mug from her. 'Perhaps *you* could persuade Ashley to join me,' he added with irony.

'If you were in a sweeter temper, she might not need to be persuaded,' Pamela retorted.

'What would I do without you to keep me on the straight and narrow, dear Mrs Flint?' he said with a suddenly wry smile and turned back to Ashley. 'Please, would you join me?'

Pamela was standing slightly behind Ross, and she winked at Ashley as he added, 'I do have something to . . . discuss with you, as it happens.'

Ashley hesitated, then walked into his office. Ross followed her and closed the door behind them.

He hung up his jacket which he'd had slung under his arm, and straightened his blue and black striped tie. 'Sit down,' he said casually.

Ashley sat, and he followed suit behind the desk. With an effort, she said conversationally, 'Did you find you couldn't tear yourself away from work, after all?'

Ross stared at his coffee-mug for a long time, and when he looked up at last his eyes were sombre and he said, 'No. I found I couldn't tear myself away from you.'

Ashley took a breath and felt her heart jolt. 'What do you mean?' she whispered.

'That's what I thought we could discuss,' he replied thoughtfully. 'The torment of our relationship.' He watched her carefully for a moment, her stunned eyes and parted lips. 'The . . . whatever it is that makes it impossible for me to do anything but work when I'm away from you. Would you, by any chance, be having the same difficulty?' His dark gaze was intent and probing.

Ashley tried to speak several times, then she licked her lips and said hoarsely, 'Yes . . . but . . .'

'Would it help if we went away *together* for a while?'

Her eyes flew to his. 'How . . .'

He shrugged. 'Well, you're already away, aren't you? And I'm supposed to be at an old shack I have on the beach near New Brighton where I was planning to spend the week fishing and relaxing, until I decided that would be impossible. Perhaps if we both went there, now, this morning, we could . . . sort some things out.'

CHAPTER FIVE

'I COULDN'T.'

'Why not?'

'I . . .' Ashley stood up and walked over to the window. 'Apart from anything else,' she turned back to him and her eyes were bitter, 'what's the point? It *is* sorted out. We've said it . . . all.'

'Have we? We've said a lot, I agree. We've never had the opportunity to be calm and reflective about it yet,' he murmured.

'Can you be that?' Ashley countered. 'Forgive me if I find it hard to believe, but . . .'

'Then I give you my word.' He stood up. 'It'll take us about three hours to get there—you can come in your own car, if you like, so you can leave whenever you like.' He held her gaze steadily. 'There'll be no coercion—and the sea-water will be good for your ankle. Even if we only achieve a way to live together in the same district and under the terms of the trusteeship, it would be worth it, but . . .'

'Ross . . .'

'Let me finish—perhaps, if we just spend a day or two being as companionable as we once could, if we make a pact to try to be . . . ordinary together, we might get things into some sort of perspective.'

'And you wouldn't try to . . .?' Ashley stopped incredulously, because she couldn't believe she could even be contemplating this.

'Try to?' he queried. 'Make love to you?' he said, his eyes lingering on her suddenly pink cheeks. 'No—unless you wanted me to . . .'

'So you could have the pleasure of knocking me back again,' she whispered, turning away jerkily.

'Ash, look at me,' he said quietly, and when she did at last, unable to veil the mixture of hurt and hostility in her eyes, he went on abruptly, 'I'm sorry . . . for that. I guess it would be fair to say I have a—devil riding me in that respect.'

Their gazes locked and held, and Ashley realised she was breathing quickly and terribly lightly as the implication of his words sank in.

'I . . .'

'But I'll do my best to keep him under control. Will you come?'

'I . . .' She swallowed. 'Maggie won't know where I am. If anything happens to Susie . . .'

'You know as well as I do that Susie's safer with Maggie, not to mention Bob, than anywhere. You wouldn't be leaving her otherwise, would you?'

'No, but . . .'

'And you'll be closer, in fact, than you would at the open day.'

'Ross . . .'

'You could also ring in as often as you wanted and leave the number. There's a phone connected—will you come?'

*   *   *

Travelling in the opposite direction to the one
she'd planned for that morning, following a blue
car towards the coast, Ashley nearly panicked
several times and turned tail. There would be no
way he could catch the Jaguar—if he were so
minded. But she knew he would not.

I don't know what to think, why I even agreed,
she thought. How *can* this help? How can it be
anything but sheer torture? I spent five years
longing for Ross, and telling myself he would
never understand. I was right, but all the same I
came back to test it out—does hope never die? Is
that why I'm doing this?

She gripped the steering-wheel and narrowed
her eyes against the sun, wishing she could force
herself to relax.

'And be . . . ordinary,' she whispered. 'Oh,
lord!'

'I don't suppose you brought swimming togs?'
Ross said with a faint smile. 'Didn't think of that,
but the shop up the road might have some.'

They'd not long since arrived, and he'd
stopped at the shop about two miles up the road
for provisions. Ashley had waited in her car.
Now, as she stood on the veranda of his shack
which was right on the beach while he searched
for keys, she was looking around, unwittingly
entranced by the beauty of the spot.

'Ashley?'

'Oh,' reluctantly she drew her gaze back from
the shining sea, the golden white, seemingly

quite private curve of beach, the small, wooded headland nearby, 'actually I do have one with me. I was hoping to find a motel with a pool.'

'Good!' He opened the door and said with a wry grin, 'Welcome to my castle. You can have the bedroom, I'll use the divan in here. Why don't we have a swim, then I'll make you a late lunch?'

'Sounds . . . lovely!' she said, with a strained smile, but although he shot her a probing glance he said nothing.

'Through here?' she asked.

'Mmm. Make yourself at home—have a look round first, if you like.'

She did. There were only three rooms in the old wooden house: a bedroom, bathroom and the main room, which opened on to the veranda and doubled as a kitchen, dining-room and lounge. A door from the bathroom led out to a back veranda which housed a washing-machine and a stone tub. Down the steps on an overgrown lawn was a washing-line and a small shed. There was also a delightful medley of trees and shrubs in the back garden. A lemon tree heavy with fruit, a rampant, purple bougainvillaea growing over the shed with fuller, plumper bracts than she'd seen for a long time and, beneath the tank stand, a riot of red and yellow canna lilies. The air was heavy with the somnolent drone of bees.

But, if the outside of Ross's beach-house could lend itself to being called a shack, the inside was more civilised. The bathroom was functional and the tiling looked new, a pristine white. The bedroom, she discovered, had honey-coloured panelled walls, a gleaming, sealed wooden floor and a comfortable-looking bed with a luxurious, padded quilt in a clear, true, jacaranda blue with a navy border on it. Other than a small bedside-table, there was no other furniture—or so she thought, until she noticed a handle on the panelled wall and pulled it tentatively to find it opened a cupboard door that revealed hanging space, some drawers and a shelf with a mirror above it, complete with a light.

She raised her eyebrows because the carpentry was expert, and she wondered if it was Ross's handiwork. Then she crossed to the door to the lounge, closed it and put her small case on the bed and opened it. But for a moment she hesitated and wondered if she should unpack, wondered if it was a gesture she was not yet quite prepared to make. Instead, she extracted her swimsuit, towel and a blouse from it.

After she'd changed, she hesitated again, standing in the middle of the room in her ivory one-piece costume that was superbly designed and shouted expense and elegance, then shrugged on her buttercup blouse, buttoned it up and went to join Ross.

He'd changed too, into a sky-blue pair of shorts, and was kneeling on the floor unpacking the groceries he'd bought. 'Won't be a minute,' he said with a glance over his shoulder. 'What do you think?'

Ashley looked around and realised that the same honey panelling was repeated in here. It also had the same gleaming floor, but with a dhurrie rug. There was a comfortable cane lounge suite painted a rusty red, with cream cushions, and a matching red glass-topped cane table and two bentwood chairs. The divan had a knobbly cream fitted cover, but it was the kitchen end of the room that really caught her eye. It was as spick and span and compactly fitted out as a ship's galley.

'I'm . . . surprised,' she said. 'Did you do it all?'

'I've been renovating it for a long time, mostly at weekends.'

'I'd no idea you were such an accomplished decorator and carpenter.'

'Then you approve?' He stood up and came towards her.

'Yes . . .'

'Good. Let's go for that swim.'

The water was heavenly, and after surfing the waves for a while Ashley lay in the shallows with silvery wavelets gently rippling over her legs. The sky was a pale blue dome hazy with heat, and everything glinted under the force of the sun: particles like minute diamonds in the sand of the beach, the windows of Ross's shack, dark green shiny leaves on the headland, but most of all the sea, like a rippled mirror.

She closed her eyes, but for a moment it was all

there behind her eyelids before it changed to
swirls of red and gold.

Then Ross dropped down beside her on his
front and said quietly, 'It's magic, isn't it?'

She opened her eyes and squinted at him. He
was very close and his dark hair was plastered to
his head. There were droplets of water clinging to
him, and the skin of his shoulders was smooth
and quite tanned for someone who worked
indoors.

'Do you come here often?' she asked idly.

'I have been lately, although sometimes I don't
get here for months at a time. My decorating has
put on quite a spurt since . . .' He stopped.

'Since I came back?' she said huskily.

He glanced at her, but his expression was hard
to read and she coloured faintly and sat up. 'Since
summer came, probably.' She hugged her knees.

'You were right first time, but let's not go into
that—yet. I promised you a late lunch. Coming?'

She looked up and he was on his feet, holding a
hand down to her. She took it and he helped her
up, and they were standing face to face, very
close; the memory of how it felt to be held in his
arms flooded her body, as if her senses had a
mind of their own, as if the feel of the tall, hard
length of him, the strength, the way his hands
and lips had moved on her once, was blueprinted
somewhere deep within her subconscious, as was
her response.

She trembled inwardly and took her hand
away. 'I should have another swim, I'm all sandy

now . . .'

'There's a fresh-water shower in the back garden. Come.' He turned away and picked up both their towels, leaving her with no clue whether he was affected the way she was. She hesitated, then followed him.

The shower was warm but away from the sun, and operated by a string-pull. She stood under it first on the grass, and felt the sandy saltiness sluiced away.

'Good idea,' she said brightly. 'Do you ever have a problem with water?'

'Only in a drought. I don't use much.' He stepped under, pulled the string and looked around. 'I must get the lawnmower out and do a bit of gardening, otherwise I'll be overrun.'

Ashley followed his gaze. 'I'll help, if you like.'

'I didn't bring you here to work.' He released the string and dried himself off. 'You're supposed to be using that stick anyway, aren't you?'

She grimaced. 'I feel like a geriatric—it was the doctor's idea, not mine.'

'All the same, you'll do as you're told while you're here,' he said with a grin. 'I can be just as militant as Maggie, you know. So for starters, inside with you, Ashley Crawford! Where you'll sit down and rest your ankle while I make lunch.'

Ashley grinned back ruefully. 'Why do I feel as if I've jumped from the frying-pan into the fire?' But she complied after she'd changed into shorts, and it struck her while they ate cold meat and salad and drank a lovely, refreshing cup of tea

that, despite what his nearness on the beach had
done to her, she was insidiously relaxing. It also
struck her that Ross was going out of his way to
make her relax, perhaps helped by the peace and
beauty of the spot, the sea and the fact that she
was feeling pleasantly tired after her swim—but
yes, he was.

And, when she yawned twice, he said, 'Have a
sleep.'

'What will you do?'

'Might even do the same.'

But when she lay down on top of the jacaranda-
blue quilt, just before she drifted off to sleep, she
wondered if he knew how easily called up,
despite the effort he was making to relax her, her
awareness of him was. And her last thought was,
why does Ross do this to me? Still. How strange
that it's never changed . . .

The sun had set when she woke, but the world
was still bathed in its orange glow, although the
sky was darkening to violet.

'Sorry,' she mumbled, coming out on to the
veranda to find him sitting in a basket chair with
his feet up on a low table, sipping a can of beer.

He raised a quizzical eyebrow at her face,
which still bore the imprint of the pillow on one
side, and the way she was still blinking sleepily.
'You must have needed it. I even mowed the
lawn, but it didn't wake you.'

She sat down opposite him with her hands
dangling between her knees. 'I don't know about

that—I feel awful. I never sleep during the day, and now I know why.'

He laughed quietly. 'A quick dip in the sea might cure that.'

Ashley raised her eyes heavenwards and shivered.

'No, it would. You'd just make it before the light goes.' He stood up and handed her her costume, which she'd hung over the veranda rail to dry.

'You're a sadist,' she grumbled. 'I'm all for swimming when it's lovely and hot, but it's cooled down now and . . .'

'Ashley,' he took her by the shoulders and turned her towards the doorway inside, 'get changed. I promise you that you won't regret it!'

Regret it she didn't, after the shock of the initial plunge which left her spluttering. Nor did he allow her to stay in long, although he said, when she came out shivering, 'A sprint up the beach would complete the cure, but I'll let you off that. Here.' He wrapped her in her towel and took her hand.

'Do I have to have a cold shower now?' she enquired plaintively.

'How do you feel?'

'Wide awake!'

'Not grumpy and foggy?'

'I wasn't grumpy,' she protested.

'Foggy, then?'

'Definitely not. All my senses are honed and keen, and I'm rarin' to go!'

'That could pose a problem,' he teased. 'In that case, you may have a quick lukewarm shower while I make . . .'

'While you make dinner. Ross, is there anything you can't turn your hand to?' she asked with a laugh.

'Not much,' he murmured, and dodged as she took a playful swipe at him. As he straightened, Ashley felt the laughter leave her and bewilderment take its place, and she lowered her hand slackly to her side.

'What's wrong?' He took her chin in his hand. 'Ashley?'

'Nothing,' she whispered. 'I . . . nothing.' She tried to look away and suppress the shuddering little sigh that escaped her.

'Tell me,' he insisted quietly. 'Don't shut me out.'

'I . . . I can't believe this is me—*that* was me. I haven't felt like that for . . . so long.'

'Then our plan is working,' he said.

'Your plan.' She moved away and he let her go.

'It can only help, Ash.'

'Can it, Ross? I wonder.' She put her hand to her mouth and stared out over the darkened sea.

'What you need is a drink now, to warm the cockles of your heart.'

She unpacked after her lukewarm shower.

It only took a couple of minutes, because all she'd brought were jeans, a couple of blouses, a nightgown and a change of underwear. But she set her toiletries out on the shelf in the cupboard and smoothed on a body lotion. Then she put on fresh jeans, a white silk blouse and brushed her hair. Apart from some moisturiser, she left her face natural, but she stared at herself in the little mirror for a moment. The weeks of working outdoors had left her with a golden tan which showed up the grey of her eyes quite startlingly, and if she was thinner, she also looked fit, she thought. But I miss my hair, she mused. Maggie was right, perhaps it was my crowning glory—I miss the luxury of being able to brush it and wear it up or down . . . I feel less feminine without it.

She grimaced at her reflection and, taking a deep breath, went out to join Ross.

He'd set the round table and there was the delicious smell of fish frying in a light golden batter coming from the stove.

'Don't tell me you went fishing this afternoon while I was sleeping!' she said.

'I wasn't going to mention it,' he said over his shoulder with a grin. 'And perhaps I should say that I often fish here without catching a thing—I just got lucky this afternoon.'

'Oh, I believe you—where many wouldn't,' she said gravely. 'What can I do?'

'You could toss the salad.'

There were tomatoes, lettuce, capsicum, raw mushrooms and even beansprouts. 'Mmm,' she said appreciatively as she added French dressing, 'what a feast. Even warm rolls and crisps! I'll get fat if I stay here too long.'

'I can't imagine that,' he murmured. 'There's also a bottle of wine, but in the meantime how about a Scotch?'

'Why not,' she said lightly, and looked around. 'Can I use the phone?'

'Sure.'

By the time she'd spoken to Maggie and Susan, dinner was ready and he was waiting for her at the table. 'You'll have Maggie agog with curiosity,' he said as he pulled out a chair for her.

'Why?' She unfurled a napkin.

'There was something mysterious about the way you said "a friend".'

Ashley shrugged. She'd told Maggie she'd bumped into a friend and changed her plans. She'd also given her the phone number in case of emergency. 'She should be pleased. She didn't approve of me going to that *fly-blown bash*, as she put it, anyway.'

Ross grinned. 'Maggie has very definite ideas on what a lady should and should not attempt. How's Susie?'

'Fine,' Ashley said. 'She . . .' She stopped.

'Go on,' Ross said, and poured her a glass of chilled white wine and sat down opposite her.

Ashley hesitated and glanced across at him. 'She's dying to show you how Georgie can shake hands now,' she said quietly.

Ross said nothing for a moment, and when they looked into each other's eyes his were sombre. 'She's extraordinarily appealing for . . . another man's child.' He looked away and down at his plate. 'For that matter, so is Natasha. How is she?'

'Fine—according to her last letter, but missing Cornflower fistly, then us.'

He raised an eyebrow and smiled slightly. 'We'll have to start giving some thought to that young lady's future. Has she anything in mind other than show-jumping?'

Ashley ate a mouthful of cooked-to-perfection, flaky fish. 'Not so far, but she's got three years of school left. You know, she's pretty bright. I mean academically. She gets great reports.'

'Did her father have any ambitions for her?'

'Only that she should be happy—this fish is marvellous, Ross.'

'Thanks. How's the ankle?'

Ashley wiggled her foot. 'At this point in time, feeling good,' she said gravely.

His lips twitched. 'So are you—looking good, anyway,' he murmured.

'There seems to be some magic in the air here,' she commented. 'Unless it's the wine on top of the Scotch . . .'

'Perhaps you're giving it your best shot.' His eyes held hers.

Ashley sipped her wine reflectively. 'I never was much good at fighting you. Will,' she paused, 'this be the answer, do you think?'

'It's got to be an improvement, hasn't it?'

'Yes . . .' But there was an unwittingly wary look in her eyes which she was unable to hide.

If he saw it, he said nothing further on the matter. In fact, he changed the subject adroitly. 'Tomorrow, I thought we might go for a drive to Brunswick Heads.'

'And leave paradise?'

'It's here to come back to and I need some paint. You could help me choose the right colour.'

'What are you painting?'

'The shed and . . .'

'But what about the bougainvillaea?' she objected.

'I'll be very careful with the bougainvillaea, and the outside window-frames. You may have noticed that peculiar sulphury green on them?'

Ashley thought for a moment, then nodded.

'That's the undercoat.'

'I see.' She finished her dinner and wiped her mouth with the napkin. 'Can I help? I could sit down and paint some of the window-frames.'

He glinted her an amused look. 'Certainly. Coffee?'

'Thank you.'

After he'd washed up, he brought out some colour charts, and between them they chose a sage-bush-green for the shed, because that was the colour he had in mind for the shack eventually, and white for the window frames.

'It will blend in with the background rather nicely,' Ashley said, 'besides being practical.' She stopped and yawned, and then looked comically surprised. 'I can't be sleepy again,' she murmured.

'Why not? It's nearly ten o'clock.'

'That late? Well, that's not so late, but I had no idea . . . time was passing so quickly.' She looked confused.

'Besides,' he said, coming over to her and looking down at her meditatively, 'you're overdue for a break. All that hard work has caught up with you.'

'You might be right,' she agreed after a moment, and uncoiled her feet which she'd tucked beneath her, to stand up. Only that was a mistake, because he didn't move away and, once on her feet, they were very close.

She took an uncertain breath as she stared up at him, and licked her lips. It was very quiet, with only the muted sound of the surf to be heard outside and inside, a moth fluttering against the shade of the only lamp on. Fluttering like her heartbeat, she thought. He's doing it to me again . . . Deliberately? What does this do to him, this closeness . . . or is he made of iron? I broke through it once, but at such a cost, and last time he . . . no . . .

Her head drooped wearily, as much in a bid to escape that dark, shuttered, steady gaze as from an overwhelming sense of futility, and she said huskily as she moved round him, 'Goodnight, Ross. Thank you for a lovely dinner.'

He let her go with only a murmured goodnight himself, and she walked into the bedroom, closed the door and leant back against it tiredly. Two can play that game, she thought bitterly. If this is how he wants it, this is how he'll have it. But then again, she mused with the bitterness replaced by self-directed mockery, what choice do I have?

To her surprise, she fell asleep quite quickly.

She woke before dawn to a sense of unease and of being heavily burdened, of thrashing about in a sea of despair and incomprehension.

She lay for a while actually physically feeling as if she was lying beneath some weight, so much so that she scrambled out of bed with her heart beating heavily and her mouth dry. I've got to . . . think, she told herself. I can't go on like this. I'm . . . the crazy part is that I'm becoming dependent on his . . . goodwill, even. Laughing and clowning at whim, *his* whim, offering to help and then . . . and then coming up against the brick wall of his . . . what is it?

She sighed and stared around in the dark, and suddenly decided she had to get out into the open, on to the beach, to walk or at least to sit and think.

It was easy to slip out; Ross didn't stir and the world outside was caught in that pre-dawn calm she was coming to know well. That time just before the first birds started to wake, and when it was often warmer than just after the sun rose.

She stepped on to the beach cautiously, her eyes gradually adjusting to the dark, and she found a small sand dune with tussocky grass growing on top like a frill of hair. She sat down at its base and hugged her knees, staring at the faint white lines of the breakers and for a time, let the peace of the hour claim her.

'His . . . utter self-containment,' she whispered at last. 'Yes, that's what it is.'

She stared out to sea, unseeing of the first faint rim of light on the horizon, and realising she'd at last put her finger on that quality in Ross she'd fought against for so long. The quality that had enabled him to keep her at arm's length for so long, although he'd admitted she'd meant the world to him, and was still able to employ . . .

'So that I never knew how much I meant to him—still have to doubt it,' she murmured. 'But assuming I *do* and did, how does he do it—why does he do it? Can he not see my fears and doubts and . . . understand that it caused some of what's happened?'

So intent was she on her thoughts, she didn't hear the birds stirring, and then a possible answer slid into her mind and she went quite still as she examined it and wondered why she'd never thought of it before . . .

What scars did Ross bear from his unorthodox childhood? He'd never shown any, he'd told her about it factually and unemotionally, and with a sort of wryness as if to say—that was life! But in his heart—does he guard his heart carefully now? she asked herself. Is *that* why I can get so close and no closer? And then I too . . . abandoned him in a sense. Oh, why did I never think . . . Because I was always so caught up with my insecurities and lack of confidence, because he was always so self-assured? Did I mistake his aloofness for disinterest when it was in fact . . . a kind of wariness? Did I fail him as his mother did?

The more she thought about it, the more it seemed to make sense. Ross had relied almost exclusively on himself to get where he had. Not only had he jackerooed during his vacations, but he'd worked nearly every free minute during term at one job or another, and used every ounce of his considerable will-power to save enough to buy the law practice. And now he was reaping the rewards; but had nearly a lifetime of fighting for what he wanted, of transforming himself from an abandoned child into a successful businessman and more, been a high price to pay, emotionally?

He said . . . everyone has their point of pride, didn't he? Was that really his? An inability to admit he needed anyone? If so, where does that leave me? she asked herself. It was hard enough then, but now . . . Unless—wanting me here like this must mean something. Can I have the patience to accept it?

The sun came up and she sat on, almost motionless, but with a new feeling of . . . not serenity, she thought, but at least a feeling of understanding, as if I'm no longer pitting myself against him as helplessly as . . . that moth last night. It's strange, she thought, I only ever wanted two things in my life—some admiration from my father, and Ross, and although I sometimes feel as if I've been to hell and back and I can never have my father's respect . . . the other hasn't changed. I wondered, after Laurie died and I decided to come back, if I would find it was a schoolgirl thing I'd grown out of, if it had been a matter of pride which was, perhaps still is, one of my failings; but no, I think not. There's something about him I can't tear myself away from—I wouldn't be here, otherwise.

She sighed and he said behind her, 'You're up early and deep in thought, Ashley.'

She jumped and turned. 'Oh! I didn't hear you.'

He was wearing only his sky-blue shorts and he sank down beside her. He was also squinting, as if the light of day was hard to take as yet; his hair was ruffled, there was a blue shadow on his jaw and he didn't look particularly impressed with anything.

Ashley gazed at him for a moment, then had to look away as her heart was flooded with sudden tenderness and her breasts actually felt heavy with longing—a longing to hold him and soothe away his early morning ill-humour.

She said, however, as she plucked one of the frilly blades of grass beside her, 'I know what you need.'

He raised an eyebrow.

'Your very own panacea for all ills.'

'My what?'

She hid a smile. 'Your cure-all for . . . grumpiness and fogginess—you know, the one you recommended to me last night. The one you *forced* me to sample.'

She saw a reluctant smile twist his lips, and he looked at her with a sudden glint in his dark eyes. 'Oh—that one,' he murmured.

'Uh-huh. I can vouch for its effectiveness,' she said softly.

'Can you now?' he drawled. 'Then you won't mind . . . sampling it again, with me?'

'You didn't do that last night,' she pointed out. 'You led me to my fate, then left me to brave the icy waters alone.'

'All the same, I'll be quite comfortable here . . . sunk in my moody depths which can take hours to disperse,' he warned and added, 'Unless you agree to come in with me.' He lay back lazily.

'I'm not dressed for swimming.' She was in fact wearing her jeans and silk shirt from the night before.

'It would take about twenty paces to rectify that.'

'You are a sadist, you know.'

'I know,' he agreed. 'Especially first thing in the morning. Ask Pam.'

'I don't have to, I've seen it. Well, if I have no choice . . .'

'None.'

'Let's add a bit of spice to it. Bet I can beat you out past the surf . . . and back to shore.'

He groaned and sat up.

'After I've changed, naturally . . .'

'Good lord,' he said bitterly, 'all these years and I never knew you were one of those bright, early-bird kinds of people!'

'Ross,' she said with a grin, 'there's a lot you don't know about me.'

CHAPTER SIX

THEY bought the paint and had lunch in Brunswick Heads at the pub, but when they got back Ross decided against starting on the shed.

'Between the two of us, we might finish the window-frames this afternoon—there aren't a lot of them. Ready to start?'

'Yes, sir! Er—you wouldn't have an old shirt I could borrow?'

'I sure would. Now listen, you start on the ones that open on to the veranda. You can sit on a stool and reach for the most part. Take a break whenever you feel tired, and I'll bring a radio out for you to listen to. Here you are.' He handed her a paint-splattered white shirt.

'What will you wear? This looks like your lucky painting shirt.'

'Nothing,' he said with a grin, and when she blinked he added, 'but my hat and shorts—sure you wouldn't rather be lying on the beach, sunbaking?'

'Quite sure,' she said firmly. 'I'd be bored to tears in no time. Hand me my brush and I'll show you what a delicate hand I have for this.'

It took them just under three hours to finish, and they shared a beer to celebrate.

'You've got paint on your chin,' he observed,

touching his finger to the spot.

'You've got paint all over you,' she countered.

'A session with the turps should cure that.'

Several minutes later, she said, 'Here, let me. It's on your back, too.'

She dabbed at the splatters of paint he couldn't reach with the rag and, when she'd finished, stared at the long muscles of his back for a moment, then said the first thing that came to mind. 'I think we need another swim . . .'

He turned and took the rag and the bottle of turps from her. 'I think you might be right.' But he didn't move and there was nothing teasing in his eyes at all, just . . . A query? she wondered, feeling suddenly shaky and finding it hard to breathe. Had the moment come? Had she breached his defences at last, but long before she'd expected to in her new understanding of him? Would he draw back again, though, leaving her humiliated and so vulnerable once more?

It was she who moved first and veiled her eyes, perhaps belatedly, and she said in a curiously uneven voice which she seemed to have lost control over, 'A swim or a shower. We both reek now.' She stared over the veranda rather blindly, then her eyes widened and she swung back, genuinely distracted. 'Ross—it's going to rain! Look at that storm building up out at sea, and it's been so hot . . . oh, no! All that work!'

He put the bottle and rag down, and said wryly and quite normally, 'With any luck it will hold off for a couple of hours, and it's very fast-drying exterior paint. But I guess we should get our swim in now. Coming?'

They lingered on the beach for a while, watching the fireworks out to sea which, together with the sun setting behind them, created the atmosphere of a heavenly war being waged.

'I can't believe the colours,' Ashley said wonderingly as they sat side by side on the sand. 'Or the . . . eerie air of expectancy, as if the world is holding its breath.'

'Perhaps it is,' he commented. 'That's quite a storm.'

'Will it . . . blow us away or anything like that?' she asked light-heartedly, to cover a sudden spurt of nervousness.

He glanced at her and smiled slightly. 'That would be an adventure, but no, I doubt it. The old shack is really solid beneath its raggedy exterior.'

'Not so raggedy now. It's amazing what wonders a bit of paint works!' She stopped and shivered as a breeze swirled across the sand, ruffling and lifting it, only to die almost at their feet.

'Cold?' he queried.

'A bit,' she said, which was not untrue, but not the only reason she'd shivered. For a long time she'd had a fear of storms, perhaps something to do with the fact that the night her mother died had been a storm-laden one, and the two things, storms and a foreboding of the loneliness to come, had become inextricably bound together.

She'd also managed to let no one know of this weakness—even hoped she was conquering it at last. But this one could be a test, she thought, then thought again almost immediately, how ridiculous! I'm not *alone* in it.

Ross said, 'Let's go in, then. It is cooling down fast.'

And Ashley heard herself reply casually, 'What a pity I didn't bring a camera. You could get some spectacular shots. OK. What culinary delights have you in store for me this evening?'

'Wait and see,' he drawled and helped her up.

Darkness fell as she showered and changed into jeans again, and this time her buttercup blouse. The storm stayed out to sea.

She rang Maggie and chatted to Susie for a time, then they sat down to dinner, a mixed grill tonight with another bottle of wine. But Ross, who'd put on his black polo shirt over a pair of white shorts, seemed disinclined to make conversation.

'Are you going to stay for the week?' she asked, then bit her lip.

He looked thoughtful, then shrugged. 'I don't know. What about you?'

'I couldn't. I don't want to leave Susie for that long. She . . . is still a bit insecure about people going away.'

He said nothing, then got up to make coffee, leaving Ashley wondering miserably if her backing away from that query in his eyes earlier

had set her back miles. Patience, she reminded
herself, and if you could only relax again, as you
did today before . . . it happened.

She pondered that while she drank her
coffee—her genuine relaxation earlier in the day,
not the up and down jumpiness of the day before.
But she had to acknowledge it had gone in the
face of how he was now, and the wretched storm
hanging about and getting closer now—and she
could feel her muscles tautening and knew she
was going to jump up and offer to do the dishes
because she just couldn't sit still any longer.

Surprisingly, he acquiesced, although with a
rather penetrating glance, and he took a torch and
murmured something about checking up outside
and perhaps moving the cars out from under the
tree they were parked beneath.

Ashley stared at his retreating back, then forced
herself to concentrate on what she was doing.

It was half an hour before he came back, and
the first raindrops were falling tentatively on the
roof. Ashley was washing the small area of tiles
before the stove and sink on her hands and knees.

He stood over her with raised eyebrows. 'You
don't have to do that.'

'I felt like it.' She tossed the cloth into the
bucket of soapy water and knelt upright.
'There—all done.' She rubbed her forehead with
her wrist, and winced as a clap of thunder
sounded overhead.

He frowned and said softly, 'Ash—what's
wrong? You're not afraid of a bit of thunder and

lightning are you? Not you . . .'

She stared up at him, her grey eyes shadowed and with a nerve beating in her jaw. Then she looked away and sank back on to her heels.

'Ash?' He knelt down beside her, his eyes narrowed and probing. 'You were the bravest girl I ever knew.'

She smiled twistedly. 'Was I? Well, I'm sorry to have to tell you this, but there are two things I've been scared of for a long time. Thunderstorms are one. But I'll be all right. I don't . . . scuttle under beds or into cupboards.'

'Two?' he queried, barely audibly.

'I shouldn't have . . .'

'Why not?'

'It doesn't matter.'

'Yes, it does.' He took her shoulders. 'Why can't you tell me?'

'B-because,' her voice shook, 'you wouldn't understand . . .'

'On the contrary, I might be able to help. Ash, I'm not letting you up until you tell me,' he said harshly. 'What's the other thing you've been afraid of for a long time? Look at me,' he commanded, and shook her.

Her head fell back and she stared up at him mutinously. Then a crack of thunder shook the air, her lips parted and she whispered into the unnatural silence as the rain held off, 'Losing you . . .'

She saw the flare of shock in his eyes, felt his fingers dig into her shoulders—and then it started to pour as if the heavens had opened and the noise on the old tin roof was terrific, but she heard him say beneath his breath, as he pulled her into his arms, 'Oh, Ash . . .'

A tidal wave of tears rose up in Ashley as it thundered and poured and lightning split the sky—reaction perhaps to the months, years of strain, but also to the intensity of the last few months—and those two words which she didn't know how to interpret. And because her nerves had got the better of her, and because her plan, formulated only that morning, to try to understand Ross better and forget about herself, had floundered so soon . . .

'Ross, oh, Ross,' she choked, 'don't . . .'

But he got to his feet, drawing her up with him, then he picked her up in his arms and took her over to the settee.

She clung to him fearfully, saying his name again anguishedly as he sat down with her and held her hard against him. 'Ash, don't,' he murmured as he stroked her hair. 'You'll make yourself sick. Stop now . . .'

She lay against him, shuddering and trying to get herself under control, and gradually the slow rhythm of his hand on her hair, the feeling of protection of his arm around her, worked until at last she was still, save for the odd unsteady breath. And, as if it was in tune with her emotions, the thunder and lightning moved inland, leaving only steady, soaking rain in its wake.

She said huskily at last, 'Sorry . . . both storms have passed now, I think.'

His hand left her hair and he tilted her chin up and stared into her grey eyes with their still wet lashes for a long, wordless moment. Then he said, 'Mine hasn't, I'm afraid. It's only just begun . . .'

He lowered his head and started to kiss her.

Surprise held her rigid for a moment, then her lips parted beneath his and she felt herself drowning in the taste, the feel of him . . .

What followed happened mostly in silence. Ross said nothing when the kiss ended, and she was too afraid to break the spell, unable anyway to speak as he slowly undressed her.

He loosened the buttercup blouse from the waistband of her jeans first, and slid one hand beneath it while he stroked the nape of her neck hypnotically with the other. She felt his fingers beneath her blouse searching for a bra, then, because she wasn't wearing one, exploring her upper body, her slender back, circling her breasts but not touching them, soothing and gentling her skin slowly and with infinite care until she closed her eyes and sighed softly with pleasure. Then that caressing hand moved down and he flicked open the stud of her jeans and slid the zip down to reveal the soft, slight mound of her stomach above the lacy white bikini briefs she wore. She turned her face into his chest and tensed expectantly, but he only continued to stroke her above her briefs, until she relaxed to a mindless, almost purring pleasure again. And when he started to inch her jeans down over her hips, she helped by wriggling, even looking up at him with a faint, rueful smile, because they were not the easiest to get out of. Finally the jeans lay on the floor and he turned his attention to her long bare legs.

I should be doing something, she thought dimly, instead of just accepting this heaven . . . do I have the courage? Then she immediately forgot her thoughts, because the soothing quality of what he was doing was changing. Her skin was coming alive beneath his wandering hand; she wanted to move to the rhythm of the way he was caressing her; her senses were awakening and clamouring for his touch to be more intimate, yet shrinking because even the most delicate touch would be almost unbearable, she thought, as her skin trembled and she was racked with a sudden shudder of desire.

His hand left her body and her eyes flew to his, but they were unreadable and she tensed again, violently this time, waiting for another rejection to come, going cold with fear.

He saw the fear in her eyes, closed his own briefly and, gathering her close again, kissed her until she relaxed.

Oh, thank heaven—she said the words in her mind, and in her relief and love found the courage to express herself physically . . .

She freed an arm and slid it around his neck, slipping her fingers into his hair, and she moved against him gently, wanting to love him and be loved more than anything in the world.

It was only gradually that she realised her mistake. In fact it wasn't even that so much—that understanding came to her much later. What she did become aware of, as she tried to tell him with her body and her hands on him, of her love, was *his* sudden tension, although it wasn't the strain of rejection. It was the opposite—a desire for her he couldn't reject but he could control, a desire to drive her to the limits of passion and ecstasy and mindless submission. And her softened, trembling body submitted helplessly to all he did, while her mind cried out with the knowledge that this was another kind of rejection, after all . . .

But before she realised it she knew only that a sudden urgency had come to him, and with an abrupt movement he lifted her off his lap so that she was kneeling on the floor between his legs.

She took a startled breath, but he was intent on unbuttoning her blouse and taking it off, and when it fell to the floor their eyes locked briefly, then he slid his hands under her arms, drawing her forward. His eyes were hooded now, intent upon her breasts and the way they moved in tune with her accelerated breathing. She knew, in the moment before he lowered his head, what he was going to do to them, and felt her nipples harden in anticipation of his tongue and teeth on them, of the savage pleasure he was about to inflict on her. But still she gasped and tautened, then made a queer little pleading sound in her throat. He took no notice until she was quivering with desire and arching her body against his hands, her eyes closed, her head back, her palms feverishly stroking his shoulders.

Then, at last, he raised his head, but only to lay a devastating trail of kisses on the lovely line of her throat, the soft hollows at the base of it.

'Ross, Ross . . .' She formed his name, but no sound came and, anyway, she didn't know what to say—whether to beg him to stop this exquisite torture or to beg him to give her the ultimate release.

Then she realised he was lifting her to her feet, and she could only cling to him as he half carried her to the divan and swept away the knobbly cream wool cover and the pillow.

The sheet was cool beneath her as he laid her down on it, but he didn't join her immediately. Instead, he stared down at her body for a long moment, then with precise, unhurried movements, although he was breathing hard, he removed her bikini briefs.

Some strange impulse prompted her to try to hide her nakedness from him with her hands, but the gesture brought a cool smile to his lips and he sat down beside her, grasped her wrists and laid her arms at her sides. He looked into her grey eyes and spoke for the first time.

'It's too late for that, Ash.'

'Ross . . . oh, Ross,' she whispered, 'what are you doing to me?'

'Making love to you, making up for all those

years when you let another man do it. Do you,' his gaze roamed her body, then lifted to her eyes again, 'want me to stop?' He traced a line between her throbbing breasts, his fingers moving slowly and tantalisingly lower and lower.

Ashley turned her cheek to the sheet so he wouldn't see her tears. 'No . . .'

And so he continued, and her tears and despair were no match for the pleasure he brought to her, sometimes with the lightest touch, sometimes with a brooding, sombre look until she was totally abandoned to desire again. Then the look in his eyes changed and she knew that if she said to him, stop now, Ross, he would not be able to, that he was as committed to the act now as she was and no other motives claimed him, that she was giving him as much pleasure as she was receiving—that the union of their bodies was now just that. Two people united at last.

She cried out twice. The first time was in involuntary pain, and he held her hard and kissed her gently until it subsided, then he began to move on her again, driven by his own need, but carefully, lovingly, until she responded and they came together in shuddering ecstasy. Her cry was soft and wondering this time.

It was ages before he spoke, and by then he was lying with his arms around her, her head on his shoulder. He said huskily as he smoothed her hair 'Why did I hurt you? Has it . . . been that long?'

She could only nod beneath his hand.

'I'm sorry,' he murmured, and traced the outline of her mouth, then kissed her eyelids. 'All right now?'

'Oh . . . yes,' she whispered.

'Can you sleep?'

She tensed and her lashes lifted. 'Where . . . are you getting up?'

'Do you want me to? It's not a very wide bed.'

'No . . . Stay, please.'

'I will—but I'll get us a cover first.' He eased himself away from her, and she closed her eyes and slipped her hand under her cheek.

He came back first with the jacaranda cover from the other bed and a couple of pillows, then two glasses of the wine they hadn't finished.

'Comfortable?' he murmured when he'd helped her to sit up a bit so she could drink her wine.

The pillows were soft, and the down of the jacaranda cover feather-light on her body. 'Mmm.' She nodded and he slid in beside her.

They sipped their wine in silence for a while until he said suddenly, 'Do you remember the summer we got enough rain to fill Sydney Harbour?'

'The summer you couldn't drive around the property without getting repeatedly bogged? Yes.'

'I've got the feeling this summer will go out in the same style. Which means more storms.'

Ashley sipped her wine. 'I'll have to . . . build up my mental defences.'

'I never knew about that.'

She listened to the rain on the roof. 'I never wanted anyone to know. It seemed so . . . silly.'

He looked into her eyes, and a faint smile touched his lips. 'It's not an uncommon phobia. I have one myself.'

'What?'

'Confined spaces—claustrophobia.'

Of the heart? Ashley wondered, but she said quietly, 'Can you trace its cause? I associate storms with the night my mother died.'

Ross put his glass down on the floor and turned to her, sliding an arm beneath her shoulders. 'I used to wonder about your mother sometimes, and how much you missed her.'

'She wasn't . . . very happy.'

'Your father was—no, I won't say it.'

Ashley smiled slightly. 'I can guess. Did . . . was it the orphanage that inspired your claustrophobia?'

'Possibly,' he said wryly. 'Not that I was ever locked into broom cupboards or anything like that, but there was the knowledge you couldn't . . . just leave, and now it's transferred itself to similar situations. Lifts and aircraft, for example.'

'Ross,' she said involuntarily, 'I don't know how you . . . coped so well, so brilliantly, in fact. I don't suppose everybody's childhood is trauma-free, and I guess I'm the perfect example of how

. . . confused and twisted up you can get, but you . . . you seem to have flourished in spite of much worse . . . well, at least I had a home and roots and financial security until . . .'

She trailed off and stared at him with a frown in her eyes. 'How did you do it?' she asked.

He considered for a while. 'I guess when you've been to the pits,' he said slowly at last, 'when you've felt like a helpless pawn—I don't mean I was ever physically abused, in fact a lot of people went out of their way to . . . make life easier, but,' he paused and Ashley unconsciously held her breath, 'when you have that feeling you don't belong to anyone at all, you—at least I did, I think—compensate with an "I'll show everyone I amount to something" kind of attitude.'

'Oh, Ross,' she whispered and reached out to touch his face. 'You did—you have! Has it . . . helped?'

'It's given me some satisfaction,' he said. 'Sure. A lot, actually,' he added with a grin. 'But I guess . . . it's not the whole answer.'

Their gazes caught and held, until she lowered her lashes and said very quietly, 'You mean marriage?'

'That, and . . . some roots. Some place of my own. I have this, but it's more of a hideaway. What I sometimes feel I need is a property where I can put down those roots, and at the same time exercise that part of me that is called to the land.'

'You should—because you do. I mean, you have a feel for it. I don't for one minute doubt you're right about the weather—you always were.'

He was silent.

'What . . . about your political aspirations?' she asked.

'What about them?'

'How . . . far do you want to go?'

He considered. 'I'd like to make federal parliament. After that, who knows? Time will tell.'

It was Ashley's turn to be silent as she drained her glass. He took it from her and put it on the floor, and she slipped down a little beneath the covers.

'And of course there's us,' he said into the silence, smoothing her hair. 'Lovers again, but still poles apart in some respects.'

Ashley closed her eyes and turned her face into his shoulder. 'I knew . . . I always knew you wouldn't be able to forgive me,' she whispered.

'Did you? You were wrong. We wouldn't be doing this if there was a question of forgiveness between us. It's not that. It's . . . oh, hell,' he said beneath his breath, and he slid his fingers up her neck and turned her face up, 'I want you all over again. Nothing changes that. Is it . . . the same for you?'

'Ross . . . yes, but not if you keep . . . thinking of me with Laurie because . . .' She stopped, and her grey eyes were anguished.

He cupped her cheek and his mouth twisted ironically. 'At the moment, all I can think of is you. So . . . I can't even put it into words—perhaps that's the problem.' And she saw a glint of torment in his eyes in the moment before he buried his head in her hair.

Ashley trembled and wound her arms around him, suddenly not caring about anything but a desire to soothe away his pain.

And their lovemaking was quite different this time. An act of mutual need, with the urgency and his tension replaced by an intimacy of their minds as well as their bodies.

How strange, she thought, as she moved beneath his weight and held him lovingly. Poles apart, perhaps, yet so close like this. It must mean something. Is it going to be the answer? Will he . . . accept that this above all else is the true expression of what we feel for each other?

It was a shining dawn that greeted her eyes when Ashley woke. The rain had gone, but through the open doorway she could see the sparkling freshness of the still rain-drenched foliage outside reflecting the rising sun. Thre were a million birds singing, by the sound of it, and the surf was pounding rhythmically, a legacy of the wind-whipped seas of the night before.

She was also alone beneath the jacaranda cover, and when she turned her head there was no sign of Ross inside. She lay still, remembering and wondering and not anxious to move but conscious of her body and the differences in it. Not solely her domain now, as it had been for so long, and she wondered if she bore the marks of his possession of it.

Then she heard a sound and looked up to see Ross standing in the doorway, wearing only a towel wrapped around his hips. For a long moment they stared at each other, Ashley with her heart in her mouth, afraid of what she might see.

And although he smiled and came over to the bed and took her hand, she couldn't read his eyes.

'All right?' he queried.

She hesitated, then nodded.

'Like a cup of tea? It's only just made.'

'I'd love one,' she whispered, but clung to his hand until he gently released her fingers.

He pulled a table up beside the bed and set the tea and some biscuits on it. But when he'd poured two cups he took his over to the doorway and leant against it, looking out.

Ashley pulled herself up against the pillows and drew the cover up under her arms, feeling suddenly desperately thirsty—and bereft because something told her the mental intimacy of their second lovemaking had gone . . .

She knew she was not wrong when he said quietly, 'Tell me about him.'

CHAPTER SEVEN

'HE WAS . . .' Ashley stopped, cleared her throat and drank some tea. 'He was like two people. I used to think there was the . . . night and the day of him, or the dark and the bright. The clever, calculating, unscrupulous side of him, but then,' she paused, 'just when you'd sworn he was the devil incarnate, he could change and you were left wondering if he was . . . not so bad.'

'So he didn't entirely alienate you?'

Ashley sighed. 'At first, before I knew what was going on, I found him . . . well, he was amusing, sophisticated and he gave no hint that he was . . . pursuing me. I . . . just didn't think much about him, but I didn't *dislike* him, if you know what I mean.'

'And when you became aware that he *was* pursuing you?'

She drank some more tea. 'I was extremely cool,' she said quietly. 'That . . . seemed to amuse him, if anything, but it didn't amuse me. It frustrated me in a way that's hard to explain, and that's when I got an inkling . . . that I was up against a brick wall, that there was more to it. And when I realised he was spending an awful lot of time at Crawford Downs for no apparent reason, and that he seemed to be on particularly good terms with my father, I . . . had a row with my father about it. That's when he broke the news.'

'But you didn't go willingly like a lamb to the slaughter.' It was more a statement than a question, and he turned to look at her.

'No, Ross, I didn't,' she said, holding his gaze steadily.

He turned back to resume his contemplation of the shining morning. 'Tell me.'

'I—among everything else I did—I confronted Laurie and,' she hesitated, 'told him he was wasting his time because I would never love him for the simple reason that I already loved somebody else.'

'What did he say to that?'

'He said, "Where is this paragon? Is your father aware of this passion?" That was,' Ashley broke off and stared down at her cup for a while, 'when I began to sense the brick wall was also dangerous and, in retrospect, when I made a tactical error. I went to my father and told him about you.' She stopped and sighed. 'I know I don't have to tell you what he was like, but it was the worst thing I could have done, because he was then able to convince himself that he was actually saving me from something quite unsuitable. And if he did have a conscience about virtually forcing me to marry Laurie, he was able to assuage it that way.'

'Are you sure,' Ross said after a time, 'he didn't

tell Laurence Lineham about me?'

'Quite sure. That was the other . . . part of our bargain. It's possible,' she added, 'that Laurie put two and two together himself later. I don't know . . .'

'Why would he do that?'

She was silent.

'Ash?'

'Because I never changed, I guess,' she said huskily.

'Are you trying to tell me he did? After forcing you to marry him and getting you pregnant immediately? Are you trying to tell me the trusteeship was his way of bringing us together again, of clearing *his* conscience?'

She was silent.

Ross moved away from the doorway at last, and pulled one of the bentwood chairs round from the table so he could sit on the other with his feet up on it, his arms folded. 'Why did he change—if you didn't?' he said at last.

'Mainly because of his health, I think. It came as such a shock . . .'

'Did he also discover . . . how much he loved you, as opposed to wanting to add you to his stable of women?'

'He . . . he said so.'

'All the same, it must have been hell. For you.'

Ashley put her cup down and laid her head back against the pillows. She didn't say anything for a time, then she turned her head to look at him. 'The hell of it was thinking about you, hearing about you from Maggie, wondering how I could get out of it . . . Then, when my father died, the hope, but . . .'

'There was always Susie,' he said flatly.

'Well—but by that time, Laurie was . . . we knew there was no hope for him either, that it was only a matter of time.'

'I see.'

'Does it . . . help?' she asked unsteadily.

He looked up. 'Did you enjoy him . . . making love to you? Did he change enough to make it acceptable?'

'No.'

'Yet it sounds as if you became . . . friends. Something must have been forged between you for you to stay with him in his hour of need.' He said it with irony.

Ashley bit her lip and thought, nothing can erase that spectre, can it? Nothing but the truth . . . oh, do I have the courage, the strength? Doesn't it have to be said anyway, because I just can't go on living this lie?

She trembled visibly, then lay quietly, her face turned towards him on the pillow, although she was so afraid of what she would see . . .

'He . . . never made love to me. He *was* the one I . . . held off with a gun. My father's own silver pistol, in fact, that had been *his* father's—and he would have handed it down to his son, if he'd had one. It was—as I told you I once read—a very effective deterrent. It certainly persuaded Laurie

I was deadly serious, and he changed tactics for a while. Then it was too late, after his stroke . . .'

The chair Ross had his feet up on spun over backwards as he got up and towered over the bed.

'What . . . what the *hell* are you saying?' he ground out through clenched teeth.

'She . . . she's yours, not his,' Ashley whispered, her eyes wide and fearful.

'But the hair? What about that?' He stared down at her, his face pale and his mouth hard.

'Tasha inherited her father's hair, but Susie's is darker . . . because she inherited her red hair from someone else. My mother. If . . . if you know what to look for, she has my mother's colouring and eyes, also my eyes, but sometimes she has . . . such a look of you it's—well, Maggie saw it straight away.'

Ross closed his eyes and almost staggered back to the doorway, and he leant against it for an age with his head in his hands.

'Ross?' she said huskily at last.

He lifted his head, then turned to her, and there was a blaze of anger in his dark eyes. 'How could you?' he said softly, but with a world of menace. 'How dared you do that to me and the only person in the world . . . who belongs to me?'

Ashley took a steadying breath. 'I had no choice . . .'

'No *choice?*' The contempt with which he said it shrivelled her, but she took another deep breath and thought, it's now or never—since I've told him, I have to *try* to make him understand.

'Ross, I didn't know I was pregnant until after the marriage. I . . . took precautions before I . . . slept with you, but something went amiss. It was nearly three months before I could believe . . . it had happened. It was such a shock, I didn't know which way to turn. I told Laurie finally, although I wouldn't tell him who . . . the father was. I begged him to let me go but he wouldn't. He . . . he said, "If you do go, not only will you lose Crawford Downs for your father and yourself, but I'll track you down and I'll ruin the——" she hesitated, then said barely audibly, ' "the bastard who did this to you." I pleaded, I raged, I told him it was a strange kind of feeling he must have for me to have done what he'd done. He said . . . he *said*, "I know that but I'm not letting you go, we'll just have to work out a way to live with this . . ." '

'Which you accepted?' Ross said with blazing bitterness.

Ashley sighed. 'Yes,' she said dully. 'I also nearly miscarried. I . . . unless you've ever been through a difficult pregnancy, you can't know . . . it was like fighting with only a quarter of your strength. And after the miscarriage was averted—and he was so clever there, he did everything he could for me—afterwards he made me a proposition and again he was clever and, I don't know, but I *did* wonder if he'd found out it was you, because he pointed out how difficult it would be to go back to the father of this baby. How, for instance, could I prove it wasn't his? What complications could it provide for someone, to arrive pregnant on their doorstep and married to another man, particularly if he had a budding career to think of?'

She paused and looked across at Ross, her gaze tormented but curiously steady. 'Was I so sure, he also said, this man, who had not apparently raised a finger to stop me marrying him, had not even tried to get in touch, wanted me back?'

Ross swore viciously beneath his breath, and came over to the bed with something so violent in his expression, that Ashley shrank back. But her eyes never left his face.

He stopped at the foot of the bed, and with a sudden, visible effort tried to take control. 'What did you say to that? Do go on, don't stop there,' he requested sardonically.

'I . . . I didn't know what to say. Perhaps,' she shrugged slightly, 'he sensed he'd hit home . . .'

'Ash,' Ross said violently through his teeth, but she sat up abruptly, pulling up the cover as she did so, and there was a suddenly bitter glint in his eyes.

'Yes, Ross,' she said tautly, 'he did hit home. Heaven help me, I don't know if I was blind or supposed to be a mind-reader, but although I

knew how much *I* loved *you*, I didn't know . . .
how deep your feeling for me was—and, since I'm
telling you all, I *still* don't, although perhaps I
understand why now . . . But let me finish—I
don't ever want there to be anything unsaid on
my part again.'

Her eyes challenged his, and the tilt of her head
was proud.

'Go on,' he said harshly at last.

Ashley was silent for a time, then she said, 'He
was never one to fail to press home an advantage,
however slight. He then proposed a truce. He
said he wouldn't—make any demands on me,
even after the baby came and I was well enough,
without my consent. But he would care for me
and then the two of us to the best of his ability.
All he wanted was for us to live together in some
sort of . . . peace. He said I could have his
dishonourable word on that, which was generally
more trustworthy than his honourable ones. He
said he couldn't promise, however, not to try in a
more honourable manner than hitherto, to . . .
woo me. He . . .' Ashley looked unseeingly across
the room, 'apologised for the fact that I seemed to
be like a fever he'd acquired for which there was
no cure, and explained that all his life he'd been
plagued by a nature which led him to take what
he wanted by fair means or foul.'

'I,' she bit her lip and looked at Ross, 'I
agreed,' she said starkly, and closed her eyes. 'But
I did make one condition. That in two years, if I
still felt the same, he would let me go without

taking any action against . . . you. *He* agreed, he said he could never resist a challenge. It was . . . a challenge he was never destined to be able to take up.'

Ross waited, then he said, 'Is that all?'

'No,' she whispered. 'He did do everything in his power to make the rest of the pregnancy . . . bearable. He even . . . fell in love with Susie. Then he had the stroke and our roles were reversed, sort of. He was incredibly dependent on my company, and so grateful for it. That was when, as he was getting over it, we really got to know each other. Then they discovered the other disease, and he used to say he'd tilted at fate once too often. He also offered me my freedom, but I couldn't . . . I don't know how it happened, he did change and the better side of him was as good as the bad side had been dark . . . Can you understand that?' Her grey eyes were pleading, but Ross said nothing and she went on, 'However it happened, we were . . . friends, and I couldn't desert him. I was one of the few real friends he had. I also knew it was only a matter of time, and that Susie and I had . . . so much time ahead of us. There,' she pulled her knees up beneath the cover and buried her face in it for a moment, 'I've said it all . . . no, not quite. There was Tasha too, a little girl lost at first with no mother and her father dying. And there was the irony of their red hair, hers and Susie's. Laurie used to say that for him it was the final irony.'

She rested her cheek on her knees and waited as

the silence lengthened.

'Why didn't you tell me this straight away?' he said at last. 'Why did you wait . . . months before you came back, and then with no intention of telling me apparently?'

Ashley lifted her head. 'Telling you?' she said softly and incredulously. 'How was I supposed to tell you, when from the moment you laid eyes on me again you made it so plain what you thought of me? Even now, even after last night, you can't understand and you can't accept it, can you?'

'No,' he said through his teeth, 'I can't. You talk of . . . friendship and this and that . . . don't you understand I can't . . . bear the thought of it? Nor can I bear the thought of him having anything to do with my child, the child I didn't even know about! As for his final irony, don't think I don't understand what that was. It was the one thing that would enable you to keep the truth from me forever, if you chose.'

His dark eyes were so hard as they rested on her, Ashley shivered. 'Perhaps I should have,' she whispered. 'I've achieved nothing by telling you.'

'I could kill you for saying that,' he grated. 'I . . . when I *think* . . . of my own flesh and blood, and not knowing, not . . . even knowing . . .'

Ashley could only blanch and shiver beneath the full, savage impact of his hurt—and wonder fearfully what he would do to her, because he was staring at her as if he'd like to strangle her. But something wouldn't let her look away.

It was he, at last, who broke the endless moment. He turned away, and with a curiously insolent, uncaring gesture undid the towel around his waist and walked across the bathroom where he retrieved his shorts, and stepped into them. 'I'm going for a walk,' he said curtly, and with the implication that she could go to hell for all he cared.

She watched him go, then laid her cheek on her knees beneath the jacaranda cover, and wept.

It was the phone that made her lift her head at last. And it was Maggie on the other end.

'Now don't panic, Ashley, I've called the doctor—although it's probably only a little childhood ailment—they generally come on with a temperature, but she's asking for you . . .'

'Mag,' Ashley interrupted hoarsely, 'I'll be there in about . . . a couple of hours.'

'Drive carefully, now. There's no need to speed, you can trust me,' Maggie admonished.

Ashley put the phone down and stared around dazedly for a moment, then she ran on to the veranda and squinted up the beach. Ross was barely visible, a mere dot and getting smaller. She breathed frustratedly and decided there was only one thing to do—she would have to leave him a note and go.

'A mild case of tonsillitis, Mrs Lineham,' said the doctor, who had arrived at Crawford Downs the same time as Ashley. 'I promise you in a couple of days she'll be as right as rain—where's your walking-stick?'

Ashley put a hand to her mouth. 'You mean *your* walking-stick,' she said ruefully. 'I forgot it but,' she hesitated, 'I'll get it back to you.'

'I'm not the one who needs it,' he said with a grin, then turned his attention back to Susie. 'Just keep her quiet and give her a couple of these every four hours—she'll probably be sleepy anyway, and if you like I'll pop in again tomorrow.'

'Told you it was nothing to panic about, but,' Maggie looked rueful, 'she's certainly easier with you here.'

Ashley looked down at the little form curled up in her bed, and felt her heart contract. 'I wouldn't have wanted to be anywhere else. I . . . I might lie down with her for a while.'

'Good idea. I'll make you both a light lunch—it's about that time, anyway—and bring it in to you.' Maggie bustled out.

'Can I sleep in your bed with you tonight as well, Mummy?' Susie asked huskily.

'Yes, you can, darling. How's your throat?'

'Sore.'

'I bet Maggie will bring something that will slip down easily.'

'Jelly?'

'Maybe!'

It was only later in the afternoon that Ashley allowed her thoughts to roam backwards, and with a tightening of her nerves she wondered what Ross was doing and thinking, and when he would come, if for no other reason than to see his daughter . . .

She didn't have long to wait. She'd just bathed Susie and put her into clean pyjamas after her dinner, and was brushing her red hair when she heard a car.

Her fingers clenched on the handle of the brush, but Susie seemed uninterested in the prospect of visitors and sleepy again, so Ashley left her with her favourite doll beside her.

Maggie had answered the door and led Ross into the drawing-room, where she'd apparently abandoned him, for she encountered Ashley in the passage and nodded her head in that direction grimly.

Ashley hesitated and smoothed her simple print dress, then she took a deep breath and went in.

He was standing on the far side of the lamp-lit room, looking out of the window at nothing in particular since it was dark, and he didn't turn immediately, although he must have heard the door open. Ashley waited with her heart beating heavily and her mind regretting the note she'd left for him, explaining about Susie. Because, even as she'd written it, she'd known it would bring him to Crawford Downs, and now that he was here she didn't know how to face him, she'd had no time to marshal any defences and accordingly was supremely vulnerable to his anger and scorn. Unless, the thought slipped through her mind, the intervening hours had made him understand a little . . .

He turned then, and as their gazes caught and held she knew the intervening hours had made him understand nothing, and she could only look away helplessly.

He strolled across the room to a point a couple of feet away, and said her name harshly and compellingly.

She looked back and shivered, because although he was dressed casually in a pale yellow shirt, dark grey jeans and white track shoes, there was nothing casual about his expression, or the lines beside his mouth.

He said, 'How is she?'

'It's tonsillitis—nothing serious. Would . . . would you like to see her?'

'How kind of you,' he murmured ironically.

Ashley bit her lip and twisted her hands together. 'You won't . . .' She stopped.

He raised an eyebrow. 'Won't what? Tell her I'm her father? No, Ashley, I won't do that today, but *one* day she'll know.'

Ashley turned abruptly to lead the way, and Ross followed, stopping only to pick up a parcel from one of the chairs.

'Susie?' she said softly to the child who was dozing with her doll in her arms. 'I've brought you a visitor, honey.'

Susie's lashes fluttered up and her grey eyes focused on her mother, and then on the tall, curiously still figure behind her, and an expression of delight lit her little face. 'Ross,' she whispered, struggling to sit up, 'you *didn't* forget to come and see me again!'

Ashley moved aside and heard Ross expel a curiously unsteady breath before he said huskily, 'How could I ever forget you, Susie? What's this I hear about you being sick?'

'The doctor came and stuck a stick down my throat. He says I've got sore tonsils and I can't swallow prop'ly.'

'Well, it's funny you should say that,' Ross sat down on the side of the bed, 'because I brought you a book about a frog that got a sore throat and he couldn't even croak.'

Susie clapped her hands and undid the parcel he handed her. Then, as surely night follows day, Ashley thought, she begged to have the story read to her. 'I should have warned you,' she murmured to Ross. 'Would you like a cup of coffee to wet your whistle?'

When she brought the coffee back, they were deep into the story, and she stood just inside the doorway and watched them unseen for a moment with a lump in her throat and a glimmer of tears in her eyes.

'She's hot,' Ross said with a last lingering look at Susie, who had fallen asleep again. He touched her brow lightly and smoothed a strand of red hair off her cheek.

'It will be a couple of days,' Ashley murmured. 'But the doctor said he'd come back tomorrow—don't worry, I'll take care of her.'

Ross straightened. 'Yes, well, I think we have something to discuss. Should we . . . take a walk?' That way we might evade Maggie's eavesdropping tendencies,' he said sardonically.

'Ross . . .'

But the look in his eyes told her it was useless to argue.

The night was cool and cloudy, and they didn't go far. When they came to a white-painted wooden fence, Ross leant his arms on it, propped a foot on the lowest railing and said, 'It's occurred to me that we have only one solution open to us, Ashley. You're going to have to get married again, my dear, but this time to me.'

The far-away cry of some night bird was the only sound until he turned his head to her and said, 'Don't look so stunned. At least there'll be the bonus that you enjoy sleeping with me—whatever I think of you,' he added softly, contemptuously.

She whitened beneath the insult, but a glint of anger came to her eyes. 'The same could be said for you, Ross. Which is exactly why it would be insane to get married.'

'Then we'll just have to see if we can inject some sanity into it, won't we?' he said flatly.

'No . . .'

'Ashley, you've denied me my child for four years . . .'

'How can you say that?' she cried.

'Because it's true . . .'

'No, I mean, don't you understand any of what happened? Why I did it? At least if you understand nothing else, can't you believe I was . . . *afraid of what they would do to you*? Oh, heaven,' she whispered, putting a hand to her mouth, 'last night, nothing . . . nothing helps.'

'Talking of last night,' he said grimly, and with a significant, mocking little look, 'that's another aspect to consider. It actually took . . . less than what happened last night to get you pregnant before.'

Ashley drew a breath. 'Ross,' she said very quietly, 'I know what a shock this must have been for you. I do—I can understand that. I also understand . . . so much more about you now, so much I failed to understand before because I was,' she shrugged, 'young and foolish, proud and quixotic, perhaps . . . Things that made what I did worse, and it was a crazy thing to do anyway, to come to you like that just before I married another man, but . . . I made that mistake and all that followed because I thought I loved

you and because I didn't *really* know what I
meant to you. For that,' she paused, then went on
steadily, 'I think some of the responsibility has to
be yours. When you can accept that and what it
means, then you can come and talk to me about
our child, and what's best to be done for her.
Until then, I'll go on as I have before, and
nothing you can say will make me change my
mind.'

'Are you implying you understand more about
me than I do?' he queried sardonically.

'I . . . I think so,' she said wearily.

'Why don't you enlighten me, then?'

'Because nothing,' she whispered, and brushed
away a tear impatiently, 'nothing I say or do is
what you want to hear or know. From the
moment we . . . met again you've only wanted to
hurt and humiliate me, and now, more so than
ever.'

'All the same, Ashley,' he said softly, 'I'll find a
way to make you marry me—and now might be as
good a time as any to start . . .'

'No!' she commanded, but he straightened and
pulled her into his arms. 'Ross, no . . .' She was
pleading now, her eyes agonised in the unnatural
pallor of her face, but he took no notice and
began to kiss her brutally, his arms like bands of
steel about her.

She could only gasp for air when his mouth left
hers, and taste blood on the soft inner flesh of her
bottom lip. 'Oh . . .' It was a soft sound of pain
and despair she made as they stared at each other,

she with her eyes wide with fear, he suddenly pale beneath his tan and breathing heavily. Then he let her go abruptly and turned away savagely. 'There's something about you, Ashley, that makes me wonder whether we'd have been better off never having laid eyes on each other.'

She closed her eyes, but they flew open at the feel of his fingers on her face. 'I'm sorry about that,' he said beneath his breath, touching her bruised, swollen mouth. 'And I guess I'm sorry that I can't change the way I feel, but you know, we also can't just let things slide on. At least, *I* can't, because I've lost so much of her life already, so . . . think about what I've proposed, won't you? Because it is the only solution. I'll be back,' he added, 'and for the time being, I'll walk you back to the house.'

They walked side by side in silence, and the clouds parted and a silvery moon laid their shadows on the track. Ashley stopped as he did when they came to his car, then she turned away precipitately and fled up the veranda stairs and into the house.

She'd not expected that anything could ease her pain over the next few weeks. One day she stopped the van at the same place she'd stopped with Tasha and Susie when she'd first brought them to Crawford Downs. She got out and leant against the bonnet while she stared around. True to Ross's prediction, there had been more storms, one the previous night, and the paddocks were

steaming under the growing heat of the morning
sunlight. There was also, to the trained eye,
evidence that her and Paddy Brown's hard work
was paying off—no sagging fences in sight to mar
the rich, late summer pasture, no pot-holes in the
road which had been graded recently and laid
with a loose metalling to prevent bogging. And
there was a mob of sheep, admittedly muddy, but
fat and contented as they foraged alongside the
road.

She took a deep breath and felt her incredible
mental tension ease somewhat, almost as if
someone was loosening a tight band around her
head and heart. And she thought, this is an
achievement, it hasn't all been a disaster, coming
home . . . Surely I can take some pride in
Crawford Downs beginning to be back to its best
. . . and the part of me that will always be Ashley
Crawford, the part that has achieved this? The
part that neither Ross or my father or Laurie
could quash. Perhaps I can even apply that inner
strength to fighting Ross when . . . he comes
back.

'Ash, can I bring a friend home next hols?' Tasha
queried. 'And can her parents bring her horse
over to stay as well? She doesn't live far away and
she belongs to a pony club, and I thought Bob
wouldn't mind helping us to put up some jumps
so we could practise together—besides which,
you'll like her and . . .'

'Tasha,' Ashley admonished with a grin, 'take

a breath or you'll burst!'

'Well . . .'

'Of course you can. Who is she?'

Tasha jumped up and threw her arms around
Ashley's neck. 'You're an absolute darling! I've
got her phone number and address, so you can
check it out with her parents. I even thought I
might entice Ross out to give us a seminar, seeing
as he's such an expert. Could you ask him for me
next time you see him?'

'The next holidays are eight weeks away . . .'

But Susie was jumping up and down excitedly.
'Ask Ross to come and see me, too!' she
pleaded.

'I'll . . . see about it,' Ashley murmured, and
avoided Maggie's eyes as she changed the subject.
'Tell us all about this term so far, Tasha. We've
missed you . . .'

Tasha went back to school blithely after her long
weekend, full of plans for the coming holidays,
and it helped the state of Ashley's heart to see her
so happy. Between them, with Paddy roped in
too, she and Bob devised and set up some jumps,
and she started exercising Cornflower and taking
her over them herself to test them out.

Her state of mind over those weeks puzzled
her. It was as if she'd gone numb again, or some
subconscious sense of survival had taken over and
was allowing her to concentrate only on the
positive aspects of her life, even dulling the
suspense. The other suspense, of wondering if

she was pregnant, was spared her after only a week.

In the meantime, summer started to slide into autumn, bearely perceptibly, and because of the rain they'd had there was the prospect of good winter feed.

Ashley always appreciated the change of the seasons, especially winter to spring and summer to autumn, when the sky got bluer and the landscape was touched with gold before drying out, when the early morning nip in the air was incredibly invigorating and one's senses were attuned to the gradual changes around the countryside. Not only there, she thought, but things like seeing Bob starting a stockpile of chopped logs for the fireplaces, and Maggie, who was an inveterate pickler and preserver, starting to bring out bottles of golden yellow peaches and ruby plums swimming in their mouthwatering syrup. And also bringing out to air examples of another of her passions, patchwork quilts.

How can I feel so . . . relatively at peace? Ashley asked herself, as she walked towards the house one late afternoon.

She stopped for a few minutes to look around at the tranquillity of the scene. She was half-way between the dam and the house, and she could see the few high, rounded cumulus clouds sailing towards the horizon reflected in the surface of the water, while behind her the homestead browsed in the sunlight.

She signed quietly, but it was only a gentle

melancholy, she realised, so unlike the usual
turbulence of her emotions. Or am I in limbo, she
wondered, waiting?

He came four weeks to the day after she'd driven
away from New Brighton, and again he caught
her unawares—but this time alone.

Bob had driven Maggie and Susie into town to
do some shopping, and Paddy Brown was on the
other side of the property with the new hired
hand. Even Mary, not that she would have
dreamt of making her presence felt, was away in
Sydney, visiting her daughter.

Ashley, with time actually on her hands now
since the acquisition of the new man who came in
daily, had saddled Cornflower up and was
schooling her over the jumps, talking to her at the
same time.

'You're not a bad little jumper, you know, and
I'm a bit heavier than Tasha, but also a bit
stricter, which might be just what you needed!
I've seen you put it over your doting mistress
from time to time . . . Should we raise the gate a
foot and see how you cope?'

Cornflower didn't reply, predictably, but when
Ashley had the pole up she demonstrated her
naturally curious nature by lipping it thoroughly,
giving it a solid nudge and then standing back to
eye it almost humanly.

Ashley laughed and swung up into the saddle.
'I hope that means you approve!'

Cornflower swished her tail and proceeded as

if she'd perfectly understood Ashely's remarks about strictness and her manners towards her mistress, and would show her present rider a thing or two by popping over the raised gate with consummate ease.

'Well, well!' Ashley remarked as she patted the horse's neck, to which Cornflower responded by blowing down her elegant Arabian nose with triumph. 'Oh, I think that's a challenge you just issued,' Ashley added. 'Shall we put them all up?'

She spent another hour schooling the horse over the gradually raised jumps, and finally called it a day with a feeling of exhilaration she'd not felt for a long time.

Nor did she see Ross, lounging against a barrel until she was almost on top of him, then the mare shied as she communicated her sense of shock through her hands. Ross straightened and grabbed the bridle, causing Ashley to grit her teeth as she slid off.

'How long have you been here?' she asked tersely, suddenly thoroughly unnerved as his dark eyes wandered over her from head to foot, taking in her red and white check blouse now sticking to her body, her fawn jodhpurs and brown boots, her wayward growing hair and the sweat trickling down the side of her neck.

He took the reins from her and said casually, 'Long enough to see you haven't lost your touch. Tasha will find that a hard act to follow.'

'No, she won't—she just needs more experience.'

She glanced at him as they started to walk towards the stables, unable to help herself from taking *him* in, and wincing inwardly because he was wearing the same grey trousers and yellow shirt as on that last day. 'Are you here on business?'

'Does it look like it?' he countered.

'It is a weekday,' she murmured with a toss of her head.

He smiled dispassionately and said deliberately, 'Am I making you nervous, Ash?'

'Why should . . . no . . .' She broke off and bit her lip.

'Why should I wonder that?' he continued idly. 'I long ago realised that when you got on your high horse——' he paused, then went on softly '—it was because you were nervous and unsure of yourself.'

'I . . .' Oh, hell, she thought, did I imagine I was at peace? Or did I know that with one stroke . . . one look, he could destroy it, and beneath that false sense of almost complacency I've been waiting and cringing? 'Perhaps,' she said very quietly, but lifting her head proudly, 'I was wondering what insults and humiliation you have in mind for me now.'

Their eyes clashed across Cornflower's back, but they'd reached the stables and he didn't reply immediately. He took the saddle off and handed it to her, reached for a hose and, like most females of the species, Cornflower responded to his ministrations with coy delight.

Ashley watched with a mixture of frustration and bitterness, and it was only when the mare was dry and ready to be put into her stall that he said abruptly, 'Tell me one thing. It's been long enough now for you to know whether there might be any . . . more of my offspring on the way.'

Ashley gasped and spun away from the wall she'd been leaning against. 'You . . . you bastard,' she spat at him. 'You . . . you'd be the last person I'd tell, anyway!'

And then she was running like the wind, away from him, with only one thought in mind: to put as much distance between them as she could.

CHAPTER EIGHT

THE ONLY reason she got a head start was because Ross was left with a thirsty Cornflower still to be put in her stall and her water bucket to top up.

And she thought, as she ran, of hiding in the house, locking herself in, but discarded the idea almost immediately because it smacked of cowardice, and she was consumed with the need to outrun him, outwit him . . . consumed with a rage that would not be contained by any four walls without tempting her to smash and throw things.

In fact, such was the pitch of her frustration, she didn't realise where she was running to until she was nearly there. Then she stopped abruptly, taking deep, sobbing breaths. She doubled over suddenly with a stitch. After a few moments, she limped towards the water troughs and the small spinney at the corner of the four paddocks . . .

She soaked her handkerchief and wiped her face and neck and wrists, then wearily climbed the fence and sank down on to the still lush, cool grass beneath the trees, never doubting he would find her.

She didn't even look up when she heard a gush of water and knew he'd stopped to fix the ball

and lever system in one trough which, true
to form, had broken down. Then the wires of
the fence twanged and he was standing over
her.

'I'm not pregnant, Ross,' she said tightly, 'so
you can go away. That is . . . all you wanted to
know, isn't it?' She raised her head at last, and
her grey eyes were furious and scornful.

'No, it's not . . .'

'All right!' she flashed at him as the tension and
frustration rose in her again and she scrambled
up. 'What else?'

'Why you're in such a temper, to begin with?'
he drawled, his dark eyes mocking.

'A temper—do you really want to know?' she
ground out. 'Well, I'll tell you! Because I've
wasted *years* of my life on you! I've fought people
over you, I've cried for you, longed for you, I've
humbled myself for you in a way no woman
should have to—in bed, in other words—*your*
bed. I've . . . spent the last four weeks . . .
a-alone,' the word seemed to echo as her voice
faltered over it, but she gathered herself
immediately, 'while you no doubt have been
brooding on how hard done by you've been. And
all for nothing!'

'Nothing?' He lifted an eyebrow.

'Yes, nothing!' she said intensely. 'What else
would you call it when a man can't commit
himself . . . when he can say things like, "You
meant the world to me, Ashley," but never *be*
there when I need him, a man always holding . . .

something back?'

She glared at him, but couldn't help noticing the pale, hard-set line of his mouth, the nerve beating in his jaw. It didn't deter her, however.

'Well, I'm sorry you've had to bear the burden of this . . . of how I felt, but you'll be spared it from now on. Even I can see now that the worst thing I ever did was to sacrifice my pride for you . . . because I am proud, Ross, and proud to be so! And proud I'll be again.'

'Will you, now?' he said softly, but with a strange glitter in his eyes. 'Not too proud, I hope, to listen to what I have to say?'

'It . . .' She stared at him and her shoulders suddenly slumped exhaustedly.

'It's probably only what you want to hear.'

'There's nothing I want to hear . . .'

'Ashley, you're behaving as if you're seventeen again,' he said meditatively.

It was too much. A furious spurt of adrenalin gave her the energy to hit him a stinging blow on the cheek, but it left her almost immediately and she had no answer to the way he retaliated. He grasped both her wrists in a cruel, biting grip and jerked her against him. 'You know what you're doing, don't you?' he said between his teeth. 'You're working yourself up into an impossible state! I came here today to tell you . . .'

'Well, you left it too late, Ross . . .'

His fingers dug into her wrists. 'Shut up, Ashley! To tell you that you were right—I *was* responsible for what happened, I did . . . try to hold you at arm's length, more for my sake than yours, perhaps. I fought with myself over the ever-growing enchantment of you, because I had no faith left in allowing myself to get too attached to anyone, least of all a woman.'

'Ross . . .'

He ignored her. 'And when I found out what you'd done, and after your father . . .' A nerve jerked in his jaw. 'I congratulated myself. I told myself you might be more beautiful, more spirited and desirable than anyone I was going to meet again, but just as fickle. All the same, when I heard about the baby, I . . . was racked with guilt.'

Her lips parted and the pain in her wrists became unbearable. 'Please . . .'

He let her go and said barely audibly, 'And longing . . .'

There was silence, except for a breeze ruffling the leaves above.

'Because it should have been mine. That time,' he said with an effort, 'the dark hours of that night, the night I met Maggie and she told me, was when I began to understand what all my caution had lost me.'

'But,' she whispered, 'you despised . . .'

'I thought I did, but I couldn't quite make it . . . ring true. Nor did it help the pain.'

Ashley made an inarticulate little sound.

'But it was too late then,' he went on harshly, 'or so I figured. And I made up my mind to put it

all behind me, I even thought I had until he
died . . . and I waited, but the months went by
and there was no word. Heaven help me,' he said
slowly and with a suddenly tortured look in his
eyes, 'I didn't even realise I was doing it again,
waiting for you to come to *me*, not . . . daring to
take the plunge myself.'

Ashley closed her eyes and crumpled to her
knees suddenly.

He sank down beside her and took her face in
his hands. 'Is that what you didn't want to hear,
Ashley? Do you know where I've been these last
four weeks? To hell and back, finally admitting
the truth to myself and accepting the blame for
ever letting you go, for never making sure there
was no doubt in your mind that I loved you . . .
for being afraid to admit the depth of it to
myself.'

'Ross, Ross . . . do you really believe that?' she
stammered.

'I do now. Ash,' he drew a breath, 'I've never
told anyone this, but while I was growing up and
spending time in foster homes, and the
Donaghues were the third set of foster parents
I had, I never gave up hope that one day I'd be
like any other normal child and be able to live
with, if not two parents, real parents, at least my
mother . . . That was another reason I was
determined to make good at something, so I could
help, but when I was fifteen she came to see
me . . .' He broke off as Ashley's eyes widened.

'I thought . . . I always assumed . . . she was

dead,' she whispered.

'No. But she'd got married and . . . she hadn't told me nor had she told her new husband about me. It seems he wasn't the type to understand. She said she'd been trying to screw up her courage for some time and,' he paused and looked away, 'for the first time I saw her for what she really was, a weak woman buffeted by fate and always making the wrong choices. She'd held on to me instead of putting me up for adoption straight away, she'd let me live in hope all those years, and then . . . denied my existence. It . . . came as such a blow.'

Ashley closed her eyes in pain. 'What did you do?'

'I told her it didn't matter. If she was happy with this man, why spoil it? It was almost time for me to go my own way, anyway, and she was still so young, only thirty-three . . . She looked at me helplessly, then she told me she was going to have his child and that they were going to New Zealand to live—he was a New Zealander—but she begged me to keep in touch, because one day she hoped to have the courage to tell him. I asked her how I could keep in touch? She said I could pretend to be her nephew, and that way at least we could write to each other.'

'Oh, Ross,' Ashley breathed.

'I still write to her, but from that day . . . Ashley, over the years I've rationalised it all to myself—or so I thought. She was only eighteen when I was born, and she was left in the lurch, she *did* try for years, and now she has two other children and a husband who is . . . good to her. I've also . . . succeeded to an extent, but from that day, I swore nothing would ever again have the power to hurt me like that. As it turned out, I was wrong.'

Ashley flinched. 'I understand . . .'

'No, you don't,' he said roughly. 'What hurt most and always will, probably, whichever way I look at it—and that's what I've been doing over these past weeks—is the thought of you and what I did to you, the thought of . . . how you stayed faithful through it all, how you never . . . grovelled to anyone, how you made your choices and stuck to them.'

Ashley was silent.

'And I discovered,' he said very quietly, 'that it was *my* lack of faith that had made it all necessary. I also realised that the thought of what you'd been through hurt more than the images I'd been trying to block out of my mind for so long—you with another man.'

'Ross . . .'

He put his fingers to her lips. 'You knew this all the time, though, didn't you? You knew me better than I knew myself.'

'I knew there was something,' she said huskily. 'But you were so self-assured, while I was . . . I thought I was the one, thrashing about and lacking confidence, I thought the problem was me. Then, when I began to understand, I couldn't believe I'd been so blind or so wrapped up in myself. But,' her lips trembled, 'today you were . . .' She stopped helplessly.

He half smiled. 'I knew from your expression the moment you saw me today that you were going to fight me, that I wasn't going to get through to you without a struggle.'

Ashley blushed. 'I've been so calm since I got home from New Brighton—I couldn't quite believe it myself.'

'The calm before the storm, but that's one of the things I love about you,' he murmured. 'The fire and ice . . .' He stared down at her. 'Can you ever forgive me?'

'Yes . . .'

'You shouldn't, and not only for how I was before you left, but the things I've said and done since.'

'Now I know why . . . but in any case, although I couldn't put it into words, I always knew in my heart I was letting you down by leaving you, but . . .'

'Don't,' he said unsteadily, and took her in his arms. 'I don't even know how you can believe I love you . . . more than anything . . .' His face was pale and grim.

'Oh, Ross,' she laid her cheek on his heart, 'I believe . . .'

'I always knew I wanted to make love to you here,' he said later. 'I used to look at you during the summer you turned nineteen, and wonder if you could read my mind, if you knew . . . how much I wanted to be doing this.'

Her red and white blouse was open and she was lying in the grass with her head pillowed in his lap, her eyes closed as he stroked the satiny skin of her breasts, skimming the lacy edge of her bra cups. As he spoke, a tinge of pink came to her cheeks, which he studied absorbedly.

'Did you, Ash?'

'No.' Her lashes fluttered up.

'Why are you blushing, then?'

She considered, staring up at him, but seeing a younger Ross in her mind, wearing his shirt with the sleeves cut out of it, his thick, dark hair windblown, the faded blue handkerchief he used to wear round his neck that he'd used to wipe the sweat off his face, the dark gypsy beauty and strength of his body . . .

She closed her eyes again. 'Because *I* used to . . . dream about it,' she said softly, and raised her hand to fiddle with the buttons of his shirt, then smooth it against the hard wall of his chest. 'Sometimes I couldn't look at your hands without imagining them doing this . . . touching me like this. And then going hot and cold in case you guessed. I used to live in a mixture of terror and longing, in case you did . . . in case you didn't.'

'If only I had.' He looked down at her with a frown of pain in his eyes.

She slid her fingers up to his throat. 'Who knows? I might have slapped your face.' She touched his cheek.

A reluctant smile lit his eyes. Then he said, 'Tell me about her—was it a difficult birth?'

'It was long, but quite straightforward.'

'Why did you call her Susan?'

'After my mother—I thought you wouldn't mind, even although you hadn't known her. She was . . . kind and gentle, fun—I think Susie might be a lot like her.'

'I . . .' He paused and slid his fingers through her hair. 'I had this insane hope, you know, that she might be mine . . . When I saw her for the first time, I was looking for some sign.'

Ashley trembled. 'It's there if you know what to look for, but I can't see myself in her either. And then there was the way she took to you . . . almost as if she knew. I . . .' Sudden tears sparkled on her lashes.

'Oh, please,' he said gently, 'don't cry—it's over now, I swear.' He bent his head to claim her lips. And later, when the tears were gone, he made love to her.

They lay together in the grass for a long time afterwards, speaking little because it didn't seem necessary, until she said softly, 'My shadows have come alive at last.'

'Your shadows?' he queried, kissing her hair.

She told him. 'It seemed so strange.'

He held her away and looked at her with a frown in his eyes.

'What is it?' she whispered.

'I think it must have been mental telepathy—I could only remember that night the same way, as if . . . through a veil, and sometimes I wondered if I'd dreamt it.'

'Do you know what I think?' she said. 'I think it was our way of . . . preserving it, so that it couldn't become flawed . . . ever.'

He closed his eyes. 'Will you marry me?'

'Of course.'

But later she said, with her grey eyes suddenly serious, 'Ross, there could be problems. For you. How will we tell people about Susie?'

'We won't tell anyone yet.'

'But say I have another baby and it looks like her? People will talk, speculate, and if you go into politics . . .'

'Ash,' he captured her chin and held her close until the anxiety left her eyes, 'there are only three people this can hurt if it gets talked about: you, Susie and Tasha—not me, because you mean more to me than anything. It will never be a contest, believe me. And one day, when they're old enough and secure enough in our love to understand, we'll find the right way to tell Susie, and Tasha—that's all that counts.'

'If you're very sure . . .'

'I am. And in the meantime, on the subject of red-headed babies, we have your mother to take the credit, don't forget.'

She threaded her fingers through his and held his hand tightly.

'One last thing, before we put the subject away from us,' he said quietly, 'I think he must have known, Tasha's father, don't you? I think he did send you back to me, and for that, I can only be grateful.'

'I'm so glad you said that.' She kissed his knuckles. 'I was afraid he would always be between us.'

'No, I've laid that devil to rest forever.' And he buried his face in her hair and held her as if he'd never let her go.

They dressed at last and walked slowly, hand in hand, back to the homestead.

'Your ankle's better.'

'Mmm.'

'I've still got your stick—I intend to keep it forever.'

'Oh? Actually, it's not mine really.'

'I'll buy whoever it belonged to another one.'

'I don't think you need to worry about that, but why?'

He stopped walking and turned her to face him. 'Because it's an instrument of fate—if you hadn't been using it and tripped or whatever that morning, causing Pam to have to rescue you . . . well, do you see what I mean?' He raised an eyebrow at her.

'I do indeed.'

'I love you,' he murmured, pulling her forward so she was resting against him. 'And I want you all over again—I don't think I'll ever get enough of you. Will you mind?'

'I suspect not . . .'

'Then you'll have to be strong for both of us—otherwise we'll never make it back to the house,' he said with a glint in his eye.

'We have the rest of our lives,' she said gravely. 'And Maggie, if she's back, will be worried.'

'Lead on,' he said wryly. 'I'm in Maggie's bad books as it is . . .'

Maggie was back and in the throes of organising a search party.

'Well,' she snorted, arms akimbo, 'where the devil have you two been? I was sure you'd had an accident, Ashley Crawford, either that or Ross had . . .' She stopped abruptly, her old blue eyes narrowing and then widening, and it was in slightly, only slightly less irate tones that she went on, 'So, that's the way the wind blows! And about time if you ask me, and what's more, Ross Reid . . .'

But Ross stepped forward, put his hands around Maggie's waist and swung her up off the ground.

'Put me down this instant!' she commanded, hammering his shoulders with her fists.

'Not until you wish me all the happiness in the world, Maggie Spencer,' he teased.

'Oh, well,' Maggie said grudingly, 'I do, but mind you take care of her this time!' Then her features relaxed and she grinned impishly down at him. 'Deserted me, eh? You always were a wicked one!'

'I know.' Ross set her down gently. 'And I didn't think you'd ever forgive me for . . .'

'Hush now,' Maggie said gruffly. 'You were all

she ever wanted, but sometimes you have to fight for what you want—that's life.' She shrugged and reached up to pat Ashley's cheek, then they were hugging each other while Ross looked on.

'Dear me,' Maggie wiped her eyes with the corner of her apron, 'I really am getting soft . . .'

'Ross! Ross!'

They all turned to see Susie sprinting towards them, her face alight with joy, and Ashley watched as Ross stared at his daughter, then went down on one knee as she reached him.

'This wedding we're planning,' Ashley said to Ross the next morning, 'should we just do it with no fuss and as soon as possible?'

He raised a dark eyebrow at her. 'Not at all—unless you're ashamed of marrying me?'

'Not at all,' she repeated, and stared at him seriously.

'Then why the rush?' he enquired.

'I thought you might be able to guess,' she murmured.

'You're dying to not only . . . wed me but bed me?' he hazarded with a wicked glint in his eye.

'Something like that,' she agreed. 'I'm not sure I'm as strong as you give me credit for.'

He grinned. 'I love the sound of that, but I intend to marry you publicly and before a preacher and . . . probably in about a fortnight's time—if I can last that long.'

Ashley's eyes widened. 'You don't mean the media?'

'Certainly not. I mean a small ceremony here with both girls—we'll have to go down and see Tasha and explain *some* things to her—and a few good friends such as Bob and Maggie, the Browns, Mrs Flint—who will be going insane if I don't get in touch soon . . . What do you have to say to that idea?'

Ashley pretended to consider, then laughed softly. 'Thank you. I accept.'

He drew her into his arms and said, with a wry little smile twisting his lips, 'I know Maggie is a stickler for propriety, but she can't object if we kiss each other now and then in the next fortnight, can she?'

Tasha Lineham and Pamela Flint happened to be standing next to each other when the preacher pronounced Ross and Ashley man and wife. It was a beautiful autumn morning, and the service was being held on the lawn before the old homestead. The bride looked ravishing in an ivory dress, and carried a small cluster of ivory, pink-tinged rosebuds. Tasha and Susan wore matching misty blue dresses and small white flowers in their hair. Ross wore an austere grey suit and white shirt—and, for their different reasons, there was not a woman guest with dry eyes.

Maggie because she'd always thought of Ashley as a daughter, Mary Brown because, to her embarrassment, she always cried at weddings, Pamela Flint because of her affection for both

Ross and Ashley, and Tasha because of her deep affection for Ashley, but also another reason which she confided to Pam as she blew her nose.

'I was hoping he'd wait for me to grow up,' she whispered.

Pamela smiled, 'I think,' she whispered back as Ross and Ashley turned and stared deep into each other's eyes and the world seemed to stand still, 'they were made for each other, those two.'

VOWS   *LaVyrle Spencer*   £2.9⁹

When high-spirited Emily meets her father's new business rival,
Tom, sparks fly, and create a blend of pride and passion in this
compelling and memorable novel.

LOTUS MOON   *Janice Kaiser*   £2.9⁹

This novel vividly captures the futility of the Vietnam War and the
legacy it left. Haunting memories of the beautiful Lotus Moon fue
Buck Michael's dangerous obsession, which only Amanda Parr ca
help overcome.

SECOND TIME LUCKY   *Eleanor Woods*   £2.7.

Danielle has been married twice. Now, as a young, beautiful widow
can she back-track to the first husband whose life she left in ruin
with her eternal quest for entertainment and the high life?

**These three new titles will be out in bookshops from
September 1989.**

W◉RLDWIDE

*Available from Boots, Martins, John Menzies, W.H. Smith, Woolwort
and other paperback stockists.*

THE COMPELLING
ND UNFORGETTABLE SAGA OF
THE CALVERT FAMILY

April	August	November
£2.95	£3.50	£3.50

From the American Civil War to the outbreak of World War I, this sweeping historical romance trilogy depicts three generations of the formidable and captivating Calvert women – Sarah, Elizabeth and Catherine.

The ravages of war, the continued divide of North and South, success and failure, drive them all to discover an inner strength which proves they are true Calverts.

Top author Maura Seger weaves passion, pride, ambition and love into each story, to create a set of magnificent and unforgettable novels.

W●RLDWIDE

Mills & Boon

4 ROMANCES & 2 GIFTS - YOURS

ABSOLUTELY FREE!

An irresistible invitation from Mills & Boon! Please accept our offer of 4 free books, a pair of decorative glass oyster dishes and a special MYSTERY GIFT...Then, if you choose, go on to enjoy 6 more exciting Romances every month for just £1.35 each postage and packing free.

**Send the coupon below at once to -
Reader Service, FREEPOST, P.O. Box 236, Croydon, Surrey CR9 9E**

------------------- ✂ ------------------- *No stamp required* -------------------

YES! Please rush me my **4 Free Romances and 2 FREE Gifts !** Pleas also reserve me a Reader Service Subscription. so I can loo forward to receiving 6 Brand New Romances each month, for just £8.10 tota Post and packing is **free**, and there's a free monthly Mills & Boon Newsletter. If choose not to subscribe I shall write to you within 10 days - I understand I ca keep the books and gifts whatever I decide. I can cancel or suspend m subscription at any time, I am over18.

EP60

NAME _____

ADDRESS _____

_____

_____ POSTCODE _____

SIGNATURE _____

mps MAILING PREFERENCE SERVICE